the Gatehouse

a book about business,
a story about life

CRAIG ELKINS

Beaver's Pond Press, Inc.
Edina   Minnesota

ISBN 1-931646-99-6

Library of Congress Catalog Number: 2003104113

Cover Art: Erika Paro (www.parostudio.com)
Cover and Interior Design: Mori Studio Inc.

Printed in the United States of America

First Printing: April 2003

06 05 04 03   6 5 4 3 2 1

Beaver's Pond Press, Inc.

7104 Ohms Lane, Suite 216
Edina, MN 55439-1465
(952) 829-8818
www.beaverspondpress.com

to order, visit *www.BookHouseFulfillment.com* or call
1-800-752-3303. Reseller discounts available.

This book is dedicated to Chelsea Marie Elkins.
You are my girl, my "little spitfire that is love personified."
You are smart and kind and the best daughter
a father could ever hope to have.
I love you sweet pea!

acknowledgments

There are so many to thank, and if I have left you out, know that it is only my frazzled brain at the end of this long journey and that you are appreciated and loved. First off, thanks to Jacquie Adams and Michael for all their encouragement, support, advice and love, especially in those early days of creation. Thanks to those who gave of their time in reading parts or all of the manuscript and the marvelous comments you provided. Special thanks to Patricia Aburdene, Martin Rutte, Maida Rogerson, Joan Shafer, Debbie Crandall, Dayna Cohen, Judi Neal, Sharon Forsythe, Marcia Ellis and Steve Irons. For her multiple reviews, wonderful insight and incredible support throughout the long process, Diane Dreher deserves special recognition. Thank you, Diane, you are amazing and the world is a better place because you are here.

Erika Paro designed and painted the cover art. Thank you Erika, it is beautiful and captures the look of The Gatehouse so well. Jack Caravela and Jay Monroe at Mori Studios did a great job turning Erika's painting into a well designed cover and were very helpful in all aspects of interior and exterior book design. Milt Adams was a wealth of information about publishing and he and all the staff at Beaver's Pond Press—especially Judith—were so patient and supportive as we worked through all the vagaries of publishing a book. Thanks to Kelley Guiney for her early editing work with the book and to Cindy Rogers for her insightful finishing touches.

My family has been fabulous through all these years, offering advice, encouragement and love. My Mom—Patti Snow; Dad—Eugene (Red) Elkins, sister—Dayna Cohen, brother-in-law Wayne Cohen, cousin Debbie Crandall and her husband

Jack Preslar, and cousin Jeanine Casanova stand out. Also, Nana, thank you for watching over me. I know you are there and giving me all your love and blessings just as you always did here on earth. Ana Ballard has been wonderful, so supportive and so loving; thank you, I'll always love you. Finally, huge thanks and all my love go to my constant companion and partner who helped in ways too numerable to list, LeAnn Bornfleth.

I was falling. But it seemed like a dream, slow motion tumbling. A kaleidoscope of colors spun by, the green of the trees, the aqua blue of the ocean bouncing off the brown of the rocks, and the bright blue and white of the sky framing the cliff's edge with the faces peering down—Sarah and MJ among them. Their faces were getting smaller and smaller, but slowly, so slowly. Maybe it was a dream.

"It's not a dream," a voice said urgently. "Focus on the trees. Go through the branches and grab, scratch, claw, pull at them. You must slow your descent."

I hit the trees reaching and suddenly the speed shifted, the limbs slashed and battered, softening me for the vicious punch of brown dirt that took my breath. I wasn't spinning any more, which was sad; I liked spinning, the colors so beautiful, drizzled on the earth's canvas as I turned—now fading to black.

The voice was persistent, yet so soft and far away. The strength grew and the persistence remained until finally I could make it out. A pleasant enough voice, quiet, soothing— male, I think.

"Jack, Jack," it said slowly.

"What," I tried to say and I actually heard my voice, although I had no sensation of my lips or tongue moving.

"Jack, can you hear me clearly?"

"Yes, I think so. You're getting clearer every time you speak."

"Good, you need to get started."

"Excellent, but I have no idea what you're talking about. Get started doing what?"

"Telling your story."

"I see. Can we back up a minute? Who are you?"

"You may call me Sandor."

"Okay, what's a Sandor?"

"It is I."

"That sounds like a smart-ass comment."

"Perhaps you are right."

I waited for him to give me a real answer. He didn't.

"Uh, Sandor, you see, the way this works is when someone asks a question—like me—then the other one answers—like you. And smart-ass stuff doesn't count." I waited again. Still nothing. This guy had been to way too many negotiating classes.

"Okay, let me refresh your memory. What is a Sandor? For example, are you American, Irish, or, given my current weird feelings, are you even human at all?"

"It is not necessary for you to know at this time."

"Come again. It's not necessary for me to know at this time?"

"That is correct."

"Then when?"

"Soon."

"And how soon is soon?"

"Soon."

"Okay," I said, "let's try something new. Where am I?"

"It is not necessary to know at this time."

"All right, at least answer me this. Am I alive? The last thing I remember was falling—and it was surreal, like a dream—and then some voice telling me to wake up and head for the trees."

"That voice was me. Trying to keep you alive."

"Did you succeed?"

"It is not necessary for you to know at this time."

"Well, what should I know at this time?" I asked in exasperation.

"That it is time to start your story."

Boy, I'd walked right into that one. I decided to change my tactic. "What's the deal with the story. Why do I need to tell a story?"

"Not just 'a story.' Your story."

"All right, my story."

"Stories are the most powerful form of communication. They allow others to see the lessons and learnings in a framework they can connect with in an emotional and human way. The experience of a story engages not only the brain but also the heart and soul. You can 'take a story with you' on many levels. This is important as a teacher tries to impart a message." He paused as if to let that sink in.

"Now," he continued, *"your* story is important not only for what it will teach others, but also for what it will teach you. You need your story more than anyone."

I tried to think of something witty to say, but I couldn't. I was surprised that he had said my story would teach others. I was even more surprised when he said *I* needed to hear it. Most surprising was this inner feeling that said he was right. But I wasn't ready to relinquish control just yet. I didn't get to be CEO by allowing myself to be pushed around.

"Okay," I began, "I understand you want me to tell a story."

"Your story," he repeated.

"Right, my story. But first I want some answers. Where am I, who are you, am I alive? Let's start with those."

"Those are not important at this time."

"What if I refuse to tell my story until I get some answers?"

"You will wait a long time."

My play now. I'd bluffed and he'd called it. Where to go? I didn't have a lot of cards. No one was talking to me but Sandor. I couldn't see or move, and I couldn't walk away from the bargaining table. All that was left as a negotiator was to extract whatever I could out of the situation.

"All right. If I tell my story will you answer all my questions?"

"Yes, Jack. Now, start with your family and childhood recollections. Include the story of you and your friends seeing your grandfather doing Tai Chi in the park and your reaction to that."

My chest tightened and I swore under my breath. Dammit, that wasn't a story I wanted to tell.

"Please begin, Jack."

I took a deep breath, or whatever amounted to a deep breath in the state I was in, and tried to start. But I didn't know where to begin. Sandor sensed my unease.

"You were a boy, Jack. Just an all-American boy…"

Suddenly it clicked in and I began.

I was a boy, that was true. But all-American? I fervently hoped so. But the slant in my eyes and the tint of my skin spelled out something different. As did each trip to the supermarket or the library where my hand was tightly held by my loving, protective mother, Yoko. Yoko, from Japan, whose family was part of an attempt to destroy America, whose uncle had steered his plane through a barrage of anti-aircraft fire to explode in heavenly death on the deck of the USS Yorktown during the largest kamikaze raid in history off the island of Okinawa. Yoko, wife of my father, Ken. Ken, from Ohio, the patriot who served his Uncle Sam, and brought back a bride when he returned from occupation duty in Japan. Ken, who left Ohio when friends, family and relatives who had lost husbands and sons to the war would not, could not, accept Yoko. They settled in Davis, a small college town in northern California, just outside Sacramento.

I was born there. They named me Jack and discussed how to raise me. Clear in their vision was my education. It would be the best possible, and the demands on me would be great. They would provide the opportunity, and I would provide the sweat. Without saying the word prejudice, they taught me early on that focus and hard work would overcome the obstacles life would throw into my path. That lesson would stick with me, as would the one that said I could be anything I wanted to be, go as far as I wanted to go. And very early on I set my sights on the top job of business—CEO.

Less clear was what culture and traditions I should grow up with. Each of them had very different childhoods and each had reasons to love—as well as reject—their own past. And, of course, good cause to be suspicious of one another's cultural heritage. In the end, an uneasy truce prevailed and they allowed both cultures and traditions in our home. But Dad was at a disadvantage. I rarely saw his family. They stayed away, still refusing to accept my mother, unwilling to let go of the pain that war had inflicted. But my mom's relatives—those who still lived—were frequent visitors. They were wonderful to me and showed me moves, stretches, and poses of ancient martial arts. It made me feel powerful and I embraced their traditions and relished their visits. Until I didn't...

I was ten and had finally been allowed to run with the predominant gang of boys. We played ball, rode bikes, and pretended to be the Lone Ranger. My martial arts training had given me an edge on the baseball diamond and in make believe battles against outlaws and I was winning over most of my classmates. But not all. Some still spouted short, vulgar sayings they had heard at home about the Japanese, others suggested I play Tonto because I had experience as a half-breed. Each day I ignored them and concentrated on being American and being a pal to those who treated me well. And so it was that I toured with my new pack one hot morning. The dust from the farmers plowing outside town blew through the air, staining our sweaty faces. We skulked under eaves and small trees all the while advancing towards the green patch of park in the center of town.

As we stepped onto the moist coolness, we spied a solitary figure dressed in a loose fitting black outfit moving and posing and turning in precise, controlled movements. Several of the boys looked on curiously, but a few began to make fun of this person that stood out from the rest of the "normal" folk.

"Look at that weirdo, maybe it's a robot."

"What an old geezer. I can't believe he can still stand up at his age."

"Are those pajamas he's wearing? Let's go have a look."

The remarks continued as we got closer, but the old man paid no heed. As for me, my heart was in my throat. I knew it was my grandfather doing his daily Tai Chi. He was visiting for a few weeks, and true to his nature he never allowed anything to interfere with his physical and spiritual development. But I was mortified. If they connected him to me—as they surely would if we got much closer and Grandfather called out to me—I would be the brunt of their jokes and probably ostracized from the group. I began furiously thinking of options to divert their attention, and as panic set in I heard the bell-like sound that could save me. The ringing melody of the ice cream man's truck floated across the summer sky and I turned quickly in that direction saying,

"I'll buy."

The boys hesitated, looking at my grandfather and back at me. But not for long. I was in full gallop and they knew money and ice cream was in my direction. Soon, the whole pack of us were running full tilt away from the park and I was praying that the little bit of allowance money I had just received that day would be enough. It was, and by the time we had ordered and paid, and I had thrown up a few more boyish diversions, the park was empty.

I had been ashamed even then, but as kids can do—and adults also as I found out later—I focused on other things and tried to forget. When Grandfather died a few years later I cried for him and I cried for me. I had lost my chance to make it right.

I paused as I finished the story. I felt shaky. The power of the story was evident. But what good did it do me now? I needed Grandfather to make it right. And I wasn't going to be seeing him any time soon.

"Sandor," I called out, "how was that?"

"Excellent, Jack. You are a fine storyteller."

"Glad you liked it. Now how about a little quid pro quo? Tell me something about yourself."

"Not yet. First we must continue with your story. The day your career and your closest friendships began. Your orientation at Dynamics."

chapter **two**

It was May 21, 1972. I passed through the security gate of Dynamics for the first time as an employee and headed across the parking lot for building 23. A beautiful spring day dawned around me, but I hadn't really noticed yet. I had a bad habit of walking with my head down and heading straight for my goal. This was good for certain things, but lousy for seeing the beauty of nature. I knew I was early for the orientation, and forced myself to stop. I took a breath and looked around. A beautiful valley looked back at me. It was about 40 miles south of San Francisco and would soon be known as "Silicon Valley," but at that time it was mostly orchards. The Santa Cruz Mountains were to the west, and San Francisco Bay to the east. Smog hadn't set in yet, either, so you could actually see the beautiful views. I had to admit it was a striking area, but after another breath I resumed my walk. Beauty was one thing, but this was the beginning of my business life. My first big job. The start of my rise to the top of the corporate ladder. As I reached building 23, I glanced at my hiring letter. The orientation was in Room 2C7, starting at 8:00 a.m. The receptionist checked my temporary badge and directed me to the second floor. It was 20 minutes to eight and I was the first one in the room. I took a seat near the front, opened my employment packet and started re-reading the materials the company had sent me. They weren't particularly exciting—policies, procedures, benefits and so on—but I figured every piece of data I knew might give me an edge in the future.

I pored over the pages with a concentration that would later become legendary within the company. Finally I looked up, stretched back and tried to focus my eyes farther than nine inches in front of my nose. As I turned to loosen my back, I was startled to see three others sitting behind me. Two women and a man. I glanced at my watch: 8:10 a.m. I grabbed my hiring sheet. Yep, the time was 8:00 a.m., and the room was right. I wondered where the instructor was. Or whether one of these three was the instructor and this was some kind of offbeat orientation introduction. We each looked around the room nervously as the clock clicked over to 8:11 and still no one in the room but us. Finally, a young woman spoke up. Her short auburn hair framed a round, pretty face and she flipped it out of her eyes as she started.

"Well, I don't know what the rules are around here, but in high school I'd have been out of here five minutes ago. After all, our time is valuable too, you know."

A blond fellow with long legs and pale skin spoke up next. We all took a second look because he had a lilting, melodic accent that was pure pleasure to listen to. I wasn't sure what type of accent it was, but it sounded English or Australian.

"In my University, you could depart after ten minutes unless it was a full professor teaching the class. Then it was fifteen."

"You're Irish aren't you?" a slender woman asked. Her brown hair just reached her shoulders and as she turned towards the man with the accent it fell away revealing the graceful lines of her neck and throat. I was quite taken with her and felt myself staring. She was not glamorous: her clothes were fairly plain, her make-up light to non-existent. But her face and mouth, even the quiet, focused way she spoke drew me in. She was thin, almost delicate, but there was a vitality, a force about her. I didn't care if the other guy was Irish; I wanted to know about her.

"Yes," he answered, but before he could go on I interrupted.

"How did you know he was Irish?" I asked her. This gave me another reason to look at her and I took full opportunity, this time focusing on the eyes. They were greenish-gold with an almost impossible clarity, and framed by eyebrows that arched just enough to intrigue.

"I spent the last two years in Europe traveling and working," she replied. I was about to continue with my questions when the first woman spoke up again.

"Before we do the life history thing, let's figure out our game plan."

This caught me by surprise, as I hadn't figured that the orientation on your first job required a game plan. Wouldn't we just sit and wait until the right people showed up?

"It's a quarter after, no one's here, and I'm hungry," she continued. "I figured there would at least be something to eat here, but maybe the food is with the guy that overslept. So I say we go find our own. I saw this little doughnut shop right outside the gate. Let's go there, get a couple hot ones and some coffee and trade our stories without the threat of interruption."

We all sat slightly stunned. I couldn't believe we were even thinking it. Our first day at our first real jobs and we were going to cut?

She saw our hesitation. "Here's what we'll do. We'll write a note on the chalkboard that says, 'We figured we must be in the wrong place. Out looking for the right room,' signed, your new employees—8:15 a.m. That tells them we're go-getters, self-starters, and not afraid to go find the right answer. Plus, who's going to turn us in when they are so late themselves? We'll go hang out for an hour, come back, say we couldn't find any other rooms, and after massive apologies on their part we'll get our orientation. And it won't be so damn long."

She stood up, her eyes challenging, and looked at each of us, finally stopping to stare at the Irish fellow.

He looked back at her, nodded, then stood. "Well, why not a little adventure? I'm hungry too. Let's go."

I had to admit that her argument made sense. Still, I couldn't believe we were talking about it. The teachings I had received from my family didn't include leaving as an option in a situation like this. It felt like a scene from "Mutiny on the Bounty." In truth, though, I was a little hungry and as I contemplated what to do, the slender, brown-haired woman rose. That did it for me. I was out of my chair so fast I banged my kneecap on the low grade-school type desk I was sitting in. And off we went. I had two French crullers, a chocolate bar with custard, and four cups of coffee. I sat next to the slender woman whose name turned out to be Sarah and had one of the best times of my life. All the caffeine and sugar wound me up pretty good as well, along with a good dose of testosterone. It was two hours before we returned, and the frantic orientation instructor was getting ready to put out an All Points Bulletin. We settled down in our chairs and as the instructor began trying to catch up, my sugar/caffeine high hit bottom with a thud. Normally, I might have dozed off, risking the wrath of an already agitated instructor, but I was too excited. I kept reliving our doughnut dash, hearing the lyrical voice of the Irishman, Elton, telling us stories and MJ (our impetuous leader of that morning) snorting as the stories reached climax. Even funnier, MJ cracking herself up with her own stories and snorting in rhythm to her labored breathing. And Sarah. Smart, with a sly sense of humor and quiet, full smiles to show her pleasure at a tale. Eyes still shining, skin so clear and bright I wanted to touch her cheek just to see what it felt like. She had a habit of turning to me, as if waiting for my thoughts. As if she cared about my thoughts already. In fact, it seemed as if they all cared. I couldn't wait for the end of the day. The four of us had made plans to meet for barbecued ribs that evening.

The rib place was a little shack that MJ had spotted the previous weekend as she scouted the new company's surroundings. I slipped into the restroom as I entered and checked myself out in the mirror. It didn't seem that my first day on the job had done much damage: straight, black hair in place, dark eyes remarkably clear despite the contacts, suit and tie unstained from the morning's doughnut binge. I looked harder at my face. It had always seemed unremarkable to me, reflecting my Asian heritage and getting increasingly like my dad's each day. But beauty was in the eye of the beholder. Wasn't that what everyone said? And what constituted "beauty" in Sarah's eyes was unclear. Maybe it was someone just like me. That thought made me smile and as I exited the restroom hallway I bumped into MJ, Elton and Sarah being taken to our table.

"Good timing, Jack," Elton said as I joined them. "And what are you so all fired happy about? That smile is positively a 'beamer.'"

"I'm happy to be with people as cool as you three," I said clapping him on the back as we reached the booth.

As we settled in, my eyes caught the flash of something across Elton's chest as he bounced to a stop in the middle of the booth. He'd forgotten to remove his new company work badge.

"Elton," I said, "I have two things to say; one a comment, the other a question."

"Sure Jack, fire away."

"First, my comment. You don't need that badge to get in here. They'll serve anybody ribs."

He glanced down quickly at his chest.

"Company pride, I don't think I'll ever take it off." He thrust his rather skinny chest out to make the badge more prominent.

"And the question," I continued, still chuckling, "is why Bernard is the name on your badge, instead of Elton?"

"Well," he said with a grin, "that is a tale unto itself. Would you like to hear it now?"

Sarah and I nodded but MJ again seemed to have her own timetable as well as her own agenda.

"No, no, not now," she said impatiently. "We have other things to discuss."

"Ah, yes, let's discuss those things," Elton said politely. An eyebrow raised, he paused looking at MJ. "And what thing might we discuss first?"

"Where we're going to live, of course. This morning I heard all of you talk about your situations. Jack, you need to find a place so you can stop that long commute from your parent's house in Davis. Sarah, you want to share expenses so you can save money for medical school. Elton you're staying with a friend of the family. As for me, even though I love Santa Cruz I know I can't fight the traffic and curves over the mountain on Highway 17 every morning. So we all need to do something."

"Let me tell you what I have been looking for," Sarah spoke up. "I want to live in a home, not an apartment, with a nice yard both front and back, a big bathtub, and some character. Maybe one of those old Victorians off of El Camino."

"Well if you can afford that, Sarah, you probably already have enough to go to med school," Elton said.

"That's the problem. I can't afford it. But I don't want to settle for just a place. I want a home. So I've been looking at want ads trying to find a room to rent in a house I would like and at the same time worrying about whether I would like the people I'd be living with. What about their sleeping habits, noise, friends, parties, and so on? I knew I could find some good ones eventually, but sitting here looking at all of you, I was thinking to myself, 'why not you three?' It's true I don't know you very well, but I wouldn't know my new roommates at all. Plus, I like all of you. And the other way it would be potluck on the house. This way we could find the exact house we want together."

"I get it," Elton said. "Why should we each pay 150 to 200 dollars for a small, cheap place when we can pay 600 or 700 dollars for a place that is truly a home."

"So we pool our money," MJ continued the thought, "get a wonderful home and become roommates." She looked around. "I like it."

We stared at each other. Deep down—whether we admitted it or not—I think we were all a little scared as we started down our new paths. A new "family" would be a comfort and piece of security in our strange new world.

Elton apparently had been watching too many "Three Musketeers" movies because he thrust his hand into the middle of the table and shouted in his Irish brogue,

"ALL FER ONE"

We looked at each other then pushed our own arms forward and finished the exclamation with smiles and laughter.

"AND ONE FER ALL"

And so we decided to move in together. We went out looking for houses, sometimes together, sometimes in pairs, sometimes alone. Initially, we didn't really know what we were looking for, beyond having at least four bedrooms and a couple of bathrooms. As we searched, however, a few desires surfaced. Sarah *really* wanted that big bathtub to soak in. MJ wanted to grow flowers and plant a small vegetable garden. Elton wanted to hang a hammock between two big oak trees and set a table beside it to hold his Irish ale. I was most interested in a short commute.

We trooped around for several weeks, in and out of houses, on the phone calling about ads, stopping on the street when we saw a for-rent sign. It was lucky that I was not in charge, because I thought most places that had four bedrooms and a few baths, and weren't total dumps, were suitable for us. I recommended three of those places.

Finally it was Sarah, who said, "Jack, those places are acceptable, but not special. If we are going to call it home, it needs to be special. It needs to have qualities that make us glad to be there, that make us want to be there. It needs to resonate with our souls and uplift our spirits." She looked at me for a few seconds. "Do you know what I mean, Jack?"

I was nodding yes, but in reality I had no clue as to what she was talking about. I was just looking for a place to sleep and hold my Cheerios. I had never regarded home as a special place, although looking back I'm sure my parents probably did. It was one of the first lessons I learned from my new friends: home is a sacred place that should nourish your spirit.

It was Sarah who called me at work one evening about seven, and excitedly told me she had found our new home. I rounded up the others and we headed out there. It was only about five miles from work, so right off the bat I was happy. It was an old Victorian with a good-sized front and back yard. MJ and Elton scurried immediately around to the back to check out possible garden and hammock sites. I went inside with Sarah, or should I say I was dragged in, as she, in her excitement, grabbed my hand and pulled me up the front steps, through the porch and into the entrance hall. Then she turned and pushed me back out onto the porch.

"Look at the porch, Jack. Isn't it wonderful?"

I had to admit it was kinda cool. It ran the entire length of the front of the house, and was about eight feet deep. It had obviously been there a long time, but the wood was firm and neatly painted a quiet blue color. Several comfortable looking chairs were there as well as a porch swing with a large quilt covering it. I took the opportunity to sit in the swing and test its comfort level. It felt good and as I looked at the front yard and the trees dotting the quiet street beyond, my body relaxed and a quiet peace began to settle over me. It was my first realization that what Sarah had been saying about a home having special qualities could actually be true. My peace was soon shattered by whoops and hollers coming from the backyard. Sarah grabbed my hand again and tugged me around the side to the back.

MJ was standing with a nice looking woman of about 55, and gesturing excitedly over a patch of brown earth about ten feet by ten feet. The woman was smiling, no doubt taken in by MJ's unabashed enthusiasm. MJ turned to us, her face radiant, and talked just as fast as she could get the words out.

"It's a garden. It's been a garden and I can keep it a garden. Barbara has grown irises, asters and sunflowers, and also tomatoes, pumpkins, and snow peas. There are tools and fertilizer in the garage and all Barbara wants for them is a bouquet and a sack of vegetables when they're ready."

I assumed Barbara was the nice looking woman, and that this was her home. I wondered where she was going now. She turned to me as if she had read my mind.

"Hello, I'm Barbara."

"I'm Jack," I said and gently took the hand she offered. She squeezed my hand firmly. Her eyes were wistful and sad, but her voice was full of life.

"This is a great yard and a great house. My husband Harold and I lived here for twenty-seven years. He died last winter and I think it is time for me to move." Her eyes were misty and she paused before continuing.

"I can't bear to sell it yet, but I have been thinking for a few months that I should put it up for rent. Today, I bought a for-rent sign and a little while ago I went out to pound it in the front yard. I was still hammering when Sarah stopped in the middle of the street. Then she backed up, parked, and came over. I never did finish getting the sign up." She looked over at Sarah.

"I have to have somebody here that will love this house and be nourished by it as we were. I'm very glad the universe brought Sarah by today. I can see the love in all your faces."

She looked at me and stopped. I wasn't sure if she didn't see the love in my face, or if I wore another one of those baffled expressions. Before I felt the need to defend myself, Elton let out another whoop from the back of the yard. I turned to look, expecting to see two beautiful oaks in perfect position for his hammock. Instead I saw Elton already *in* a hammock swinging between two old trees. I took a look to see if they were oak and realized quickly that I couldn't tell an oak from a maple from an alder. Whatever they were, they were perfect for Elton.

As he swung he called out, "Jack, come on over and have a rest in here. It's just grand."

I smiled as he said that. "Grand" was his favorite adjective and as common in Ireland as "beauty" was in Canada, or "cool" was in the U.S. And the way he said it, with the vowel sounding like "ahh" and the word being stretched out, was magnificent. I loved hearing him speak.

"All right," I said, and jogged to the back of the yard. Reaching the hammock Elton had vacated, I quickly jumped in, displaying some of the athleticism for which I had been known in high school. Just as quickly, the hammock spun about and dumped me onto the grass. Barbara politely attempted to suppress her grin, while the others began tittering (Sarah), bellowing (Elton), or snorting (MJ). I was determined to recapture some dignity and quickly jumped up and faced the group with what I hoped was a suave and debonair look. But the snorts continued and as Barbara broke and her laughter started, I felt my facade cracking. Soon we were all feeding off each other until none of us could stop and the tears started rolling down our faces. I wasn't sure I wanted to be the source of the humor, but I had to admit that a good laugh felt very nice indeed.

As I stood there wondering whether to have another go at the hammock, Sarah saved me.

"Everyone, come on. Let me show you the inside." She waved her arms excitedly and ran towards the house. Of course, by now, even though I didn't understand this universe thing yet, I knew what I would find in the house. Sarah led us straight to it. A beautiful, freestanding, white cast-iron soaking tub with clawed feet painted gold and ornamental designs carved around the edges. Light filtered through a skylight bathing the tub in a soft glow, and a stenciled garden scene climbed the walls above it reaching for the skylight. A large window looked out to the backyard and several running ivy plants sat on the sill, their vines billowing out and down in a green waterfall that ended at the top of the tub. The effect was of a garden bath and it was so nicely done that even I began to think maybe a bath or two wouldn't be a bad idea. Sarah was beaming as she showed us the detail in the tub and the fixtures and how the stenciled vines mixed with the real plants offered such a wonderful effect.

It was clear now that we were going to take this place and I began to wonder what leverage we might have to negotiate after all of our emotional outbursts. And we weren't even done yet. Sarah led us all through the house, which elicited steady squeals of delight. The living room was to the right of the entry way as you walked in the house, and it looked like a room out of a magazine. It was furnished with paintings, sculptures and beautiful old furniture, (which I'm sure had a special name and period associated with it but, like trees, this was another one of my non-specialties). A bay window in the front matched the room's decor perfectly, and was comfortable to lounge in as well. A large stone fireplace completed the scene, and as brainless as I was in these areas, even I knew this was special. MJ immediately started to plead with Barbara to let us keep the furniture there. She mentioned more money and a longer lease, a higher deposit and monthly furniture "check-ups."

Barbara just listened, finally saying, "we'll see."

MJ was not ready to give up so easily and I could see her eyes looking straight up as if trying to crawl back inside her head and pull out the argument that would sway Barbara. Suddenly, my intuition kicked in and I knew what Barbara needed to hear. I also knew I needed to be the one to say it, because if she had doubts about any of us, I was pretty sure it was me.

"Barbara, this room and all that's in it is special. We will love it as you loved it and as if it were our own."

I finished the sentence and blushed deeply. I wasn't used to following my intuition except on a baseball field, and I certainly wasn't used to speaking about a room as if it were a living, feeling being. Barbara looked at me for several seconds, smiled slightly, and tipped her head in a slight nod. Sarah immediately stepped forward and took Barbara's hand and held it as she said a quiet thank you. MJ shook her head from side to side, looking at me as if I were an alien. Finally she shrugged, apparently unable to fathom where my remark had come from, stepped forward and hugged me, then turned to thank Barbara.

I went over to the bay window and sat on the cushion there. On a table next to the window was a nice cast iron magazine holder that Barbara had loaded with several home and garden type magazines. I grabbed one of them and was idly flipping through it, trying to let the color in my face return to normal, when Elton came over.

"That was a helluva thing to come out of the mouth of a practicing Neanderthal like you, Jack. What got into you?"

"I haven't the foggiest," I said truthfully. "Suddenly, I knew what had to be said, and who had to say it. So I did. I'm not sure where it came from."

"Here's a little advice," he said. "Let your instincts come to the forefront more often. Cultivate them. Then follow them. Whatever you just found, you don't want to lose it."

I trailed along as we toured through the rest of the house and the cellar. It really *was* a special house and I found myself drawn to it. I was excited about the chance to live in a home like this and with three people like MJ, Sarah, and Elton. Barbara made some tea and coffee and put out some cookies. We ate, sipped, talked, and generally had a good time. Finally, I figured it was time to negotiate. I excused myself and went out on the front porch and a few minutes later called for the three of them to join me. I knew we probably had only a few minutes until Barbara joined us, so I quickly began to lay out our position.

"All right, we aren't in great shape here, but there are a few things going for us. There is some tile that needs to be replaced, the grout work upstairs is poor, the stairs may need some work, and let's face it, Barbara is looking to..."

Sarah cut me off. "Jack, what are you talking about? What are we doing out here?"

"Deciding on our negotiating strategy. I figure we can work her down a hundred first, that will give us some room when we start adding back in for the living room furniture and..."

Sarah cut me off again, this time with a little anger. "We are not negotiating like some labor union versus management fight."

"But," I started, "we need to get..."

"Shut up, Jack," MJ interjected.

I turned to Elton for support. He was laughing at my incredible denseness as Sarah and MJ went back into the house.

"Jack, how can you be so perceptive one minute and so dense the next? You've been taking too many negotiating classes at work. Not all of life is a negotiation, you know. When you have mutual respect and caring, then you just agree on fair terms and be done with it. And you know in your heart what is fair for both sides. And often it isn't what an arbitrator would think."

As I sat outside pondering those words, the deal was struck inside. Everyone else soon came out and we stood on the porch and said our good-byes. MJ, Elton, and I thanked Barbara one last time and headed for my car. Sarah lingered there; clearly the two of them saw something special in each other. Finally they hugged tightly, kissed each other on the cheek, and Sarah turned and ran to us.

"Let's celebrate at Antonio's," she said. Antonio was a former Jesuit priest who had taught at Santa Clara University for nearly twenty years. He had been famous there for his sharp intellect, his many publications, and his ability to engage his students. Former students said he was one of the toughest graders, gave loads of homework, and wasn't at all shy about calling on you in class whether or not your hand was up. Despite these characteristics, his students loved him because he gave all of himself to his teaching, and really cared about them as people, not just students. They routinely came back to visit him, asking questions about life, or getting advice on difficult social, moral, and emotional issues.

One day he completed a book on the four Greek types of love (Agape, Eros, Phillia, and Storge), wrote a resignation letter to the cardinal and the university president saying he needed to experience all forms of love in this lifetime, packed a box and walked out the door. Within a year he had married and opened a restaurant. We had stumbled upon it and fell in love with the atmosphere, the food, the crowd, and most of all, Antonio himself. He was always there performing whatever role was needed so his customers would have a joyous experience.

We piled into the restaurant chattering happily. Antonio waved and motioned us to the back, corner booth.

"You all seem to be in particularly good spirits tonight," he said as he handed us menus. He cocked an eyebrow. "Special occasion?"

Elton and I both opened our mouths but before we could speak, MJ jumped up.

"We got a house! It's incredible, with a garden, a huge bathtub, a hammock, and a fireplace. It is so cool and we each have our own room and..." MJ grabbed Antonio's hand and did a pirouette.

"So," Antonio said, "it is a special day. How about some Chianti and antipasto to start?"

"Brilliant," Elton said. "Let's start celebrating!" And we did. By the end of the evening though, after listening to my friends and Antonio, I had something else on my mind. With Sarah and MJ in the bathroom and Elton flirting with the waitress, I saw my chance.

"Antonio," I called out. He stopped clearing the table next to ours and brought his eyes to mine. I shifted nervously. "I have a question for the great philosopher and theologian." I tried to say it as though it was just an interesting question that had occurred to me, a good test for a great thinker like him.

"What is it, Jack?" he said, dropping his dishrag and stepping to our table.

"What should someone look for in life?" I stammered. "I mean, what is important?"

"A few things come to mind, Jack, but two main ones stand out for me. Intimacy and the ability to have and express joy."

"That seems a bit simple, Antonio," I said. "Intimacy and joy?"

He looked at me gently for a moment. He knew this was more than a philosophy question.

"Intimacy in one's life, the close connection with people—family, friends, work compatriots—is really the heart of living, and, to be somewhat clever, the heart living. The heart needs that to grow, is nourished by it. And joy—the deep, deep feeling of wonder, beauty, and being so glad you are alive—is the critical element that nourishes the spirit. Joy can come from people, nature, literature, and art, and also from God, or more accurately your relationship with God. Not a religious relationship, a spiritual one. Joy should be present each day, Jack."

He looked at me for a few seconds that seemed a lot longer.

"What about joy, Jack? Does it visit you each day and do you return it twofold?"

I didn't answer. I just sat there, hoping it was a rhetorical question. Father Antonio continued and I let my breath out in a muffled sigh of relief.

"Many of us don't, Jack, because we are afraid to truly experience joy. We are afraid if we taste it, we will not be able to live if it leaves us. Fear makes our decisions for us." He smiled.

"Bad way to live." He picked up our empty basket of garlic bread and sped off to answer cries from the kitchen. I chugged my glass of Chianti and poured another.

chapter **three**

The house deal was soon finalized with Barbara's move-out date, the cleaning, and our own move-in date agreed upon. We had offered to help Barbara with the move and the heavy cleaning in the house—in exchange she would keep our rent down and allow us to use some of her furniture. A good win-win negotiation and it taught me something—look at as many alternatives as you can before you agree. Sometimes the best ones are not the most obvious. This was timely information, because my first position at our new company was with our Purchasing group. After several months of training, they had assigned me to a negotiating team that handled most of the company's major purchases.

I tackled my job with all the eagerness of a new hire and the motivation of someone who dreamed of a spot on the top rung of the ladder. And I was very lucky. I had a manager who was extraordinary. I didn't know it then, of course. He was my first manager, and I figured he was just one of a long string I would have that would be great. After all, we were a big successful company and wouldn't we promote managers because they were good at dealing with people and had been well-trained in management concepts, psychology (both individual and organizational), crisis management, large and small group dynamics and so on? Little did I know...

But Ed was great. I don't know whether he took all those courses or not, but he had a capacity for working with us as individuals, and for bringing us together as a team. I remember how he worked with me to open up my mind and let out some of my ideas.

Since I was an eager young recruit, I thought that the way to make the boss happy and get ahead was to do exactly what he or she said. This had worked well for me as an undergraduate and in my MBA program. So I listened to Ed and tried to follow his instructions explicitly. But after a while, his instructions became less structured, still very clear on the overall objective, but not so direct on the details of how to do things. For example, I would frequently develop negotiating papers for us prior to contractual talks. After the first few, Ed gave me an assignment that, looking back on it, was obviously designed to force me to begin thinking and learning more on my own. Wanting to be the perfect employee, I went to see Ed to get a few things clarified. "Ed, about this latest negotiating paper."

"Yes, Jack. Here, have a seat. What's on your mind?"

"Well, I'm clear that you want a draft negotiating paper in two weeks on the new contracts."

"Right."

"But your directions were a little less precise on some of the details."

"How so, Jack?"

I rattled off four or five areas where Ed had previously been very specific about who, what or how much should be included in the paper. I concluded with, "so, Ed, this latest assignment doesn't include that information like my first few did, and I sure don't want to do it wrong."

He looked at me and smiled. "Jack, if you don't get at least a few things wrong, then both of us aren't doing our jobs."

"How's that again?" I muttered.

"For you to learn, for you to be able to think independently and *lead*—not just follow—you must step out on your own. It is my main job to allow you to step, even if it is in the wrong direction, to be there to nudge you if needed so you or the project aren't hurt too badly, and to be a source of wisdom, not direction."

"But," I protested, "you know so much more than me. And you've been doing this successfully for years. Your direction is what's needed for us to be our most efficient and productive."

"In the short run we might operate more efficiently, Jack. But not in the long run."

"Why not?" I asked.

"Two reasons. First, a great company is built not only on quality, but quantity. Not just a few people capable of doing an efficient, excellent job, but many. I'm one, Jack, but with you, we will soon be two, and if we both mentor others we will be four and on it goes. Great companies have depth and breadth."

"And the other reason is just as critical. When we allow you to use not only the part of your brain that follows direction, but also the part that creates and innovates, we double our abilities and our chances for excellence. Maybe more than double. I've been doing it this way for awhile and my brain will have trouble breaking out of its established patterns, while you may see things in an entirely new way and radically improve the process."

He smiled again. "So use your best judgment on those questions you have, status me at our project reviews and any other time you feel it necessary, and let's learn together."

Looking back on the conversation I can certainly see the wisdom in his words. But it was what he did next that I now realize was brilliant. As I walked down the hall one morning a few days later he invited me into his office. He just happened to have a few "leftover" doughnuts on the table, and they just happened to be French crullers, my favorite. His coffee pot just happened to be steaming with a fresh pot of his personal favorite, French Roast blend, and a spare cup was already out. He poured me a cup and gave me a plate and napkin for the doughnuts. I settled in happily, with most of my usual guard dropped.

He began with a little small talk about the weather and such, then he asked me about my hobbies. 'What did I like to do in my spare time' was the way he phrased it. I stammered around a little, but before I could get too tongue-tied, he started talking.

"Let me show you one of my hobbies." He started drawing with a pen on a blank piece of paper and within a few minutes, there was a cartoon. A fellow stood on a bridge railing with a bungee cord tied around his ankles. He was labeled with my name. On the bridge deck itself was a second man labeled Ed. He was holding the other end of the bungee cord in his hand and talking to the man (me) on the railing.

"Go ahead and jump," the cartoon version of Ed was saying. "I'll have this thing hooked up by the time you need it."

The drawing was wonderful, sharp and clear, and the characters were priceless caricatures of Ed and me. Ed's full head of wavy, black hair was exaggerated into a huge pompadour, while my face depicted fierce concentration but with an enlarged right eye looking back in bewilderment at the loose rope ends. As I read the caption I burst out laughing and couldn't stop. Finally I looked at Ed.

"Does it feel a little like that now to you, Jack?" he said with a chuckle.

I wiped a tear from the corner of my eye as I nodded.

"I have to admit it does, Ed. But I'm willing to trust you."

"Good. Thanks, Jack. I trust you, too."

We continued drinking the great coffee and eating the doughnuts, and he showed me a few of his other drawings as well as another related hobby—collecting comic book versions of the classics. He showed me a Shakespeare comic book of *Hamlet*, which had remarkable color drawings wrapped around a condensed version of the Bard's play. By the time I left, I had opened up a little about my life and was feeling much more comfortable about sharing my thoughts, opinions and ideas. Which, of course, was just what I needed to do for my current assignment and for my growth in the company.

"Jack." Sandor broke me out of my reverie. "Tell me what it was like to be an employee under Ed."

I thought for a moment. "Well, I certainly remember my excitement at working with Ed, and the whole department reflected his spirit and aliveness, his humor and integrity. Deep down I knew he trusted me, and in fact cared about me. Although I couldn't have articulated it at the time, he made me feel valued and respected—even important. That translated into better work from me. Not that I wasn't a self-motivated, "self-starting," over-achieving kind of guy. I was, and I tried to over-achieve for all my managers. But I could clearly see how much more excited I was to come to work, and how I generated better ideas and solutions when I was happy, relaxed and felt trusted. And I knew employees who were not so motivated, or were lacking the confidence to really use their full potential, needed to feel respected and cared for even more."

"So as a 'first-line' manager, Ed might be a model for others to emulate?" Sandor asked.

"Yes, I suppose so," I said. "Certainly the best I ever saw."

"So in your company now, how do you train potential first-line managers to emulate Ed's style?"

"Uhh," I muttered, "I'm not sure our first level manager's course deals with that sort of stuff. I think it is mostly about policies and regulations and finance and discipline measures and information they have to know. At least it was when I went through it."

"Something to consider, don't you think? It is those first levels that touch all the people in the company. Yet the training for them is small and their burden is great as they respond to the workers and their issues, as well as answer to executives who drop more requirements on them daily."

That made a lot of sense. "Listen, Sandor, did you go to the Wharton School of Management or something? You're not bad."

"Thank you, Jack. And no, not the Wharton school. A whole different school."

"I don't suppose you'd tell me about that school?"

"Not at this time."

"Right, not at this time. Let's move on then so we can finish the story and I can get some answers."

"Good, let's do that. Continue on with your new house and new friends."

Our new house was magnificent, the long porch in front, the hammock in back looking towards the garden. On the day we moved in, furniture bounced along the walkways on the backs of friends as inside new pieces were added and shifted until the rooms were just right. The house vibrated with its own energy and it fed us as we moved through the hallways. We had named it The Gatehouse, because it opened us up to so many new possibilities. MJ had come up with the name and the rest of us liked it immediately. The Gatehouse. Symbolic of new beginnings. And I was definitely hooked on our new home. Each time I pulled up in front I felt a special joy. Maybe I was starting to understand Father Antonio's words, after all.

That first night we had a celebration in The Gatehouse. Just burgers and beer, but the taste was magnificent and the discussions fascinating. Elton had bought some special Irish ale for the occasion and as I opened my second—or was it the third—it reminded me of our postponed discussion of how Elton had gotten his name. I reminded him he owed us that.

"Right you are, Jackie boy," Elton said. "Let's pop an ale—oh, I see you've popped already—and here's the story. You know I'm Irish, and Bernard is a very common Irish name and was chosen by my parents for me at birth. And I was called Bernard all through my childhood until, in fact, I came to America. I had always wanted to see America and when I was fifteen I got a chance to be a foreign exchange student. I jumped at it."

"Wasn't it hard to leave your family, Elton?" Sarah asked.

"Very hard; we're very close. But they knew how much I wanted to see the world, and they truly believed the experience would be wonderful. So they gave me their blessing, and I completed all the paperwork to be an exchange student.

"The family I was assigned to lived outside of Phoenix, Arizona."

"Phoenix," I interjected. "That's a heck of a temperature difference from Ireland. You must have been roasting."

Elton laughed and you could see he was thinking back.

"Roasting is probably a good adjective for how I felt those first several months. The shock of stepping out of the plane and having 110 degrees hit me full force is something I'll never forget." He paused and there was emotion in his voice as he continued.

"But I wouldn't change a thing. The family that met me at that hot airport was full of extraordinary people. And I grew to love them all. Hank and Corliss were wonderful parents who treated me as one of their own. Mary, the eldest daughter, had just entered community college and tutored me in English and writing. Hank Jr., who was a year older than I, was beginning his junior year in high school, and introduced me to baseball and to his friends. And little Chelsea was a seven year-old spitfire who was love personified. It was such a grand time that I extended my stay and ended up graduating from that high school. I would spend summers in Ireland with my family and the school year with my adoptive family. I felt like I had the best of both worlds. It was grand."

He eyeballed the three of us. "I can see by your faces that you're wondering how I could have been gone from my family for so many years. And you'll wonder even more when I say I stayed there and went to Arizona State University and then applied for U.S. citizenship."

He paused to let that sink in and, as the surprised looks on our faces began to turn to questioning ones, he continued.

"It was the right thing for me," he said quietly. "I knew it in my heart, I knew it in my soul. Deep, deep, down I was positive at each step that I was making the right decision. The smartest— and the hardest—thing I have done so far in my life is to listen to myself, my intuition, in making those tough decisions."

He let a breath out and leaned back in the bay window seat, then popped forward quickly.

"And you know, that same voice told me to come here to California, to take the job at our"—he pointed to the badge that he once again had forgotten to remove—"new company, and just see what happens."

"Elton," Sarah said, "not many people listen to their inner voice, and even fewer have the courage to follow it. You should be proud."

"Well, we'll see if I heard it right. Although," he turned to all of us, "looking at you three I can't imagine it was wrong."

He held his gaze for a long moment, his eyes moving back and forth between us, but never blinking. It was a touching moment and, like so many of those, too intimate for me.

"So, are you going to tell us about your name or what?"

"Yes, Jackie boy, right away." He smiled at me, a kind smile, but knowing. "All right, I call this story 'The Day the Movies Came to Town.'

"My adopted family lived in a small town outside Phoenix. I was a junior in high school and for the last year had been work- ing at a bowling alley on Main Street. It was called Felton Bowl, after the owner, Red Felton. Now Red had come by his nickname honorably, for he did indeed have red hair; and, of course, he had no choice in his family name. But he couldn't escape the name and many folks still called him Red Skelton when they were having a little fun. If it bothered him to be compared to a rather slapstick comedian he never let it show, and, in truth, the towns- people loved him. He was a local celebrity because of his many bowling exploits which included helping to organize the

Professional Bowlers Association, winning a bunch of money and a few cars on a televised bowling show hosted by Milton Berle, and winning the 1954 Masters tournament.

"So, one day this movie company arrived. They were scouting for a small desert town with a southwestern flavor, and after some review and discussion with our civic leaders, decided to shoot several scenes there. The movie starred Ray Milland, who wasn't seen much, and a bear, which was very visible in a cage behind the volunteer fire department. Felton Bowl was a quaint 10-lane house with a great diner that had the best coffee, breakfasts, burgers and tortilla soup for miles. The movie folks soon found this out and began frequenting the diner. With great urging from me and the other regulars, they were persuaded to shoot a scene with the Bowl as the background. There was one problem, however.

"The setting for the movie was the fictitious town of San Marco, 'a small desert town teeming with secrets and a hidden past' as the promotional material described it. But the movie execs thought Felton sounded like a city name, and since the scenes were supposed to be in San Marco, they said Red would have to change the name of the bowl. I suggested they take the 'F' off Felton and add an 'S' to the end so it would read ELTONS BOWL. I even fashioned a little apostrophe to put between the 'N' and the 'S' so it would be possessive. This left no doubt that the Bowl was named after the owner, 'Elton,' and not a city, and satisfied the movie people.

"On the day of the shoot I was excited. I had my picture taken standing right below the sign (which now read 'ELTON'S BOWL'), and additional pictures taken with Red, and with a few cast members from the movie. The owner of our local weekly newspaper noticed all of this and put one of the photos of me standing in front of 'ELTON'S BOWL' on the front page of the next edition. And my new name was born. I was 'Bernard (AKA Elton)' in my high school yearbook that year and just Elton in my senior yearbook and ever after."

chapter **four**

A week later, Elton and I were in the backyard, unable to move—Elton in his hammock, of course, and me in a lawn chair. We had gorged ourselves on our first Gatehouse barbeque. Hamburgers and chicken, potato and Waldorf salad, ale and lemonade. But my two-plate gorging was nothing compared to Elton's four-plate feast. And yet if his 6'2" frame held 160 pounds, it did so only barely.

"Where did you learn to eat like that?" I asked him. "You're not planning to hibernate this winter, are you?"

He laughed. "No, although that sounds like a nice concept. Gorge yourself, then take a really long nap."

"Did you have to fight off brothers and sisters? First come, first served?"

"Well, I did have a few tussles with me brothers and sisters, but not over food."

"What was your childhood like, Elton? You hear about Ireland being a beautiful but often poor country. How was it for a kid?"

"I love Ireland and I love my family there, but it wasn't an easy place to grow up. We didn't have a lot of money and the working class neighborhoods were rough. But my family, all of them, parents, aunts, uncles, grandparents, placed a great deal of importance on hard work and education. Helping with the family business was very important so we could eat and stay dry, but no matter what the situation at work, my lessons came first. I can still hear my father's admonitions before I started school and frequently thereafter:

You can be whatever you like, Bernard my boy, but you must work hard and get educated. We've done all right, your mother and me, but the world will open up for you if you're educated.

"That sounds reasonable," I said.

"Yeah, Dad made a lot of sense. As I got a little older, he lengthened his advice to include the responsibilities and obligations that went along with a job."

"Bernard, when you agree to work for someone, you must give them all you have every day. Whether you sign a contract or just shake hands, you are giving your commitment to do your absolute best in exchange for the money and benefits they give you. Don't let anyone tell you different. If you think your value has exceeded the value of the compensation, then address that when you negotiate a new contract. If you still can't get a fair deal, look elsewhere. But never stop providing a full effort. It is not about money then. It is about your word. When you give it, keep it."

"I like that, also," I chimed in. "I think people should keep their word and take responsibility for their own actions."

Elton nodded. "Me, too, although I didn't always do it. When I got older still, Dad added one last piece to the equation."

"Someday, son, you will lead organizations or even your own company. And you will start worrying about the profit and loss numbers more and more and focusing on the bottom line. But never forget this. If you take care of the people, they will take care of the profits. And it doesn't matter whether you are managing them as part of a bigger company, or you own the business and everyone is your employee. Either way you will have special responsibilities and obligations to the people. You must pay them on time and provide appropriate benefits for your business, of course, but it goes beyond that. Their time with you, and doing your work, is the biggest part of their life. If you subtract the time they sleep, the hours getting to, working at, and returning from your business makes up the greatest expenditure of time they have. This is important. It means that if their work is not meaningful, if they don't feel they are contributing in a mean-

*ingful way, if they can't learn and grow, if they don't see the greater
good of the business, then they won't be able to engage all of themselves—body and soul— and they won't feel fulfilled at work. You
will lose them, mentally, physically, or both."*

I wrinkled my nose. Dear old dad had gone a little too far.

"That sounds too touchy-feely for me, Elton. What was your
dad, a counselor or something?"

"No, a butcher."

"A butcher?" The surprise showed in my voice.

"Yes, a butcher, and the last twenty years he has had his own
shop. Not many people work there, but all of them are happy, as
are his customers. And I think it is because he practices the principles he preached to me. At the time, I'll admit, I wasn't always
sure what he meant. But I never forgot them and now, as I enter
the workforce, I see how they apply to me as a worker, and how
our leaders could use them to be better leaders. And when I get
where I'm going, I will start with these principles and then, as I
learn, add to them."

"Ah, Elton's principles of leadership. I can hardly wait."

Elton turned red.

"Well, I have got a long way to go," he said softly.

My heart sank as I realized I'd just rejected his father's key
principle and poked fun at him, all in the space of thirty seconds.
And while I wasn't about to say I agreed with the principle, or
even thought it necessarily a *management* principle at all, I *was* feeling bad about my treatment of Elton and tried to make amends.

"Just where are you going, Elton? You've mentioned it a few
times, like you already had a plan, but I don't think I've ever heard
it. Will you tell me your plan?"

"Well, it is really more of a dream than a plan," Elton said
sheepishly.

"All the better," I replied. "If you don't have dreams you aren't going to get very far."

"Yes, that's true," Elton nodded. "All right, here it is. In Ireland, I worked several summers for a good friend of the family. He owned a small brewery that brewed lager and ale for our region."

My face must have looked puzzled because he stopped briefly then began an explanation.

"The brewery brewed beer, of course, but there are two main types of beer depending on how they are brewed. One is lager and one is ale. You might recognize them by their color and consistency. Lager is the lightest and thinnest: most American beers are lagers. Ale is darker and richer and there are categories of ale that further define how it was made and what ingredients were used and so forth. You may have heard of porter or stout, those are both types of ale. You'll know stout when you see it because it is just what the name implies, very rich, dark, and heavy. Guinness is Ireland's most famous beer and it is definitely stout."

I nodded in comprehension. I'd had a Guinness before and it was thick.

"How does something become an ale in the brewing process and not a lager?" I asked.

"Well, there are a few differences," Elton replied, "but the main one is how the yeast is introduced during the brewing process. In ale it is put in from the top and this compresses the beer and makes it heavier. In lagers it is introduced from the bottom and it makes it lighter and bubblier—if that's a word."

I nodded slowly in comprehension. I was learning about beer, but I was also learning something new about my friend. His eyes shone and his voice bounced with excitement.

"Anyway," Elton continued, still drawing pictures in the air as he tried to help me see his vision, "I loved that job. I loved working in the 'brewhouse' as the beer was made, and listening to the brewmaster as he talked about the beer-making process. I never have been a big drinker, but I loved tasting and smelling the beers, and having the first one out of a batch at the end of the day. I loved the intricacies of mixing the malt and hops, the waters and the grain. I loved the whole process. And the last few years I worked there—during my summers off from college—I was allowed to help brew the beers, and learn how to be a brewmaster."

He looked over at me, his eyes still bright and tinged with hope.

"That's what I want to do here in America. Start my own small brewery and brew the best lagers and ales around."

"Elton," I began, still feeling a little chastened, "that's a wonderful dream. You'd be so good at that, especially because you love it. You would be energized and focused because it is your dream, your vision, not someone else's. You would control the direction and the decisions, the strategies and the objectives. You could lead that company into whatever products, markets, and mergers would boost the value the most."

I was getting carried away thinking about all that power and control and, as he was so able to do, Elton brought the focus back to the critical element. One, frankly, that I would sometimes forget in my results-oriented thinking.

"Mostly, I want to begin by following my father's advice and then continuing to learn so I can lead the people in such a way that they are happy and inspired in their work; and then **together** we can lead the company towards the vision we create."

I shook my head gently in amazement at Elton's thought process. In the short time I'd known him it seemed he would always come back to people, to caring, to basic issues like respect, fairness, even love. He was like Sarah in that regard, they both said things frequently that showed a wisdom beyond their years. And though I often scoffed at such concepts when applied to business, a deep respect for Elton's commitment to those principles had started to grow in me. I thought back to my own childhood, and I knew my parents had worked hard on my values. As I contemplated that thought, Elton seemed to pick up on my vibrations.

"Jack, what do you think were your parents' principles? What were they trying to pass on to you? I'm sure they must be very special people."

"Yes, they are very special," I said softly as I thought about my childhood. "Like your parents, they were very concerned with education, and my success. They felt I could be very successful, but, because of the prevalent Asian bias, I might have to over-achieve to do it. They drummed into me the necessity of not only being the best, but being the best by a large margin. The work ethic I got from them is very strong."

"I've seen that for sure," Elton said. "You're the first in and last out many days at work, and you think about work all the time. But what about the family issues, the people side, the spiritual side? Was there a conflict there between the cultures?"

I nodded. "Yes…" I hesitated. Not only was I uncomfortable talking about my feelings in this area, I wasn't even sure I knew them. While Grandfather was doing his Tai Chi in the park, I was running away. And I had never stopped.

"Elton, I'm not sure how to explain this to you. There *was* tension with the two cultures; and my parents allowed me to see both. At first, that was great. American culture was all around me, I couldn't help but assimilate that, and my Mom's family showed me Asian traditions which I found very cool." I smiled at the recollection.

"For a kid, martial arts, body awareness, developing and controlling your power—that was heaven. Then I rejected it all because I was afraid I wouldn't fit in with the other kids." My head dropped as I remembered.

"Jack, Jack," Elton jumped to my rescue. "I'm sure it wasn't that bad. You were a kid in a tough situation."

"Not that tough, Elton," I whispered gathering my courage. "Let me tell you a story."

I told Elton the story of my grandfather doing Tai Chi in the park—and my flight from him. It was the first time I had told anyone that story and while it terrified me to let out my secrets, it was as if a release valve had been opened. Amidst the fear, tension started to leak out and although I had to hold my hands to stop them from trembling, inside I felt lighter.

But as I related how I ran from Grandfather in the story, I saw a picture of myself. Running through the park again, chased this time by a curling wave of shame that slammed me to the ground, then lingered, white foam hanging in my hair, a bitter kiss on the cheek. I choked out the end of the story and fought back the sobs. Elton reached out and put his hand on my shoulder.

"Jack, you were just a lad. Let all of the history go. You're a good man. You can do a lot of good in this lifetime." He looked at me, his hand still on my shoulder. "Why don't we talk about it? Get all the past out and then plan the future. It's not too late to re-visit your roots."

I found my breath coming in short, tight spurts. I forced my lungs open, pulled in a big pool of air, and let it out slowly. This was too fast for me. Too much openness, too much introspection, too many areas to explore where I didn't already know the answers. Exploring for me was following a crisp plan to a high probability conclusion. My culture, my traditions, my spiritual growth both now and in the future—these were unknowns of the highest order. And of the scariest type. Not to mention the pain of re-visiting my betrayals and my cowardice.

Elton squeezed my shoulder. He was looking for an answer. As I tried to push one out, a bell-like sound floated through the air and MJ bounced out of the house ringing a melodic bell. Sarah was behind her with a tray that she laid on the picnic table.

"Gentlemen," MJ said as she approached the hammock, "dessert is served." She did an elaborate turn as she reached the hammock sweeping around to head back toward the house, her hand motioning us to follow. On the patio, she cocked her head and rang the bell again.

"Now, gentlemen."

I jumped out of the lawn chair and ran for the table.

Saved by the bell again.

"Jack, your storytelling is magnificent," Sandor applauded. "Poetic and full of truth."

"I don't suppose that will get me answers to my questions any quicker," I responded.

"Not in the sense you mean, not right now. But when you are honest and complete in your story we can move along much quicker. And that will get us to the end in better time. Continue now with the Gatehouse traditions all of you started—and don't forget to talk about the 'coincidence' picnic. But why don't you start with MJ's 'name discussion.'"

That made me smile. "Okay, here goes."

We were lounging around the living room one Friday evening enjoying Barbara's furniture and the warmth of the room. Elton had commandeered the window seat, his feet wedged three feet up the wall into a nook. Feet splayed, I lay across the Persian rug looking up at MJ and Sarah at opposite ends of the couch. Conversation was light and varied until MJ, predictably, startled us all.

"I don't think I even want to work for Dynamics. Or any big company. I feel lost."

"It hasn't been that long, MJ," I said. "Give it a chance."

"I know it's only been a short time, Jack. But I do feel lost. Like I don't belong."

"What would you be wantin' to do then, MJ?" Elton asked in his Irish brogue.

"I don't know. I like cooking, I like people, I like decorating and design. I like gardens and trees, too. But I don't know how all that translates to a career, or even a job right now."

"Why don't you let us help you, MJ?" Elton asked. "We'll be your job counselors. After all, we're like grizzled veterans in the workplace now."

MJ laughed. "I'm not sure Sarah will ever be a grizzled anything, but, why not, I'm game."

MJ's willingness to try new things was a trait that I already admired in her.

All right, MJ," I said. "If we're going to help you, we'll need a little more background data."

"Sure, whatever you want," she said.

"Okay." I grinned mischievously. "What does MJ stand for?"

"Oh, no, no, no. You don't need that."

"Yes, I do," I said. "It will help me prepare my brain to think of good ideas about you."

"Yes, that's right," Elton said picking up my drift. "I need to be more in touch with the real MJ, the inner MJ, in order to really help. And to do that, I must feel like I know you better. Really know you. The first step would be to know what MJ means so we can link with your past."

MJ stared at us incredulously.

"What a crock! You guys are totally full of shit."

"You know, MJ," Sarah began, "they might be right. Knowing your first and middle names—I'm assuming the MJ comes from those two names—and why you go by MJ, might give us some insight into your character."

"Oh, not you too, Sarah," MJ moaned. "How about some sisterhood here?"

"You know, she's right," Elton said.

"Who's right?" MJ asked.

"You are," Elton affirmed.

"I am?" MJ looked startled.

"Yes, you are. Three against one isn't fair at all. Here's a better plan. Invite me to join with you. Then it will be two to two."

MJ looked at him suspiciously. "What's the catch?"

"No catch, none. You just tell me what MJ stands for and then we'll hold the fort together."

"Ding, Ding!! I see the catch now. If I tell you, you'll just tell them."

"No, I won't. Because we'll be on the same side then."

"Do I look that gullible, Elton?" MJ asked. "I mean, really."

"But MJ, you need someone on your side. Let me explain again. First..."

And off he went. When Elton got rolling he could be quite persuasive. That's why the marketing folks had recruited him so hard to join our company. He had interned there one summer during college and impressed the heck out of the department. MJ never really had a chance. Five minutes later he knew what MJ stood for and we had a new game going.

"All right, you two," I said, "Sarah and I want to know. Tell us or we'll spread false rumors around the company."

"Like what?" MJ demanded.

"Like MJ stands for Michael James and you used to be a man."

"Jack," Sarah protested as MJ tried to whack me on the head.

"Okay," I said laughing, "I won't use that one. But who knows what I'll come up with. I need the truth."

"Okay, mate," Elton said to MJ, "we can't have these yahoos spreading malicious gossip about you, now can we? Let's propose a deal."

"What kind of deal?" MJ asked.

"We'll give them three guesses as to what MJ stands for. If they guess, we confess; but, if they don't, they must hold their tongues from now until the clovers are gone from Ireland."

MJ looked around. "Do you agree to those terms Jack?"

"Sure, why not." I looked over at Sarah. "Want to give it a try?"

Sarah raised one eyebrow as she looked at me. I already knew her well enough to know she would never be a party to spreading rumors, malicious or not; but, I also thought she had a streak of fun in her and might play along with the game.

"All right," she said with a smile. "I'm in."

"Great!" I almost shouted and scooted closer to her. "Let's huddle."

"Huddle?"

"Yeah, like in football so we can decide our guesses in private."

"I'm not sure we have much to hide, but okay, let's huddle," she replied and tilted her head to mine.

"A traditional huddle works like this," I said as I laid my hand across her shoulder and neck and pulled her arm up to my shoulder. She looked me in the eyes for a few seconds.

"All right, let's do a traditional huddle."

Between the tone of her voice and the open, unflinching look, I lost my bravado and began to color. I looked down and started to talk.

"What about Mary Jo?" I stammered.

She gently chewed her lip as her head slowly started to swing back and forth. She seemed unfazed by the sudden intimacy and unaware of my discomfort. "That seems much too mild for someone to be as vehement as MJ is about not telling us."

You're probably right," I said eager to move on. "Got any ideas?"

"What about Missy Jo?" she asked. "Didn't MJ say earlier she was born in Texas? Two names like that are common in the south and..."

"Yeah," I cut in. "I know a great guy whose full name is Bill Rea, spelled R-E-A but pronounced like Ray. He told me when he visited the south and introduced himself as Bill Rea, people would ask, 'Billy Ray what?' They figured there had to be a last name attached to Billy Ray."

I laughed as I finished the story and glanced at Sarah. She chuckled, but I wasn't sure if she was truly amused or just being polite. I was definitely trying to impress her and I knew that when I tried to impress someone, as opposed to just being myself, I frequently did not leave the impression I was shooting for. I tried to think of something really witty to say, but Sarah spoke first.

"So, what do you think about Missy Jo? It fits her birthplace, and although I don't know her that well, MJ doesn't strike me as the kind of woman who would like to be called Missy."

"Sounds logical to me," I said giving up on the witty remark. "Let's try it."

"Missy Jo," we announced in unison.

"I cannot tell a lie," Elton said. "You are wrong. Two guesses to go."

"All right," Sarah said, "let me think."

"MJ," I interjected, "where in Texas are you from?" I didn't want to get on with the guesses too fast. The partnering with Sarah was much too enjoyable. Especially the huddle thing.

"Well," MJ replied, "I was born in Wichita Falls. My Mom and Dad started a small restaurant there that I really don't remember. We moved to Farmers Branch, Texas when I was four. I don't remember much about that either except we had a neighbor who owned an ice cream maker and I loved that. Kindergarten cost too much, so I had to stay an extra year in nursery school. I hated that. All my friends went off to kindergarten and I was left behind with the 'babies.'"

"How long did you stay in Farmers Branch?" Sarah asked.

"Only a few years, then we moved to Broken Arrow, Oklahoma. My father…"

"Hold on there," Elton interjected. "From Farmers Branch to Broken Arrow? You're not serious?"

"But I am, Elton. And we talked of moving to Okmulgee and Anadarko. But we didn't. We stayed in Broken Arrow for many years. My father got a job as a route salesman for a coffee company, selling to restaurants and corporate offices in several states around Oklahoma. He was pretty good at it and we were comfortable. But I always wanted to get out of Oklahoma and live by the ocean. When I turned 18, I got out a map, looked at how far away the Atlantic and Pacific were from Oklahoma, decided they were about equal and flipped a coin. When the buffalo came up, I headed west."

"Buffalo?" Elton questioned.

"Yes, I flipped an old buffalo nickel. I thought it only appropriate that the buffalo side would be west. So I moved to Santa Cruz, got a place on Ocean Street—which coincidentally is just a few blocks from the ocean—and started enjoying the sun and the surf."

"All right, that's enough history," I said. "Sarah, let's re-huddle and figure out the name of the wandering soul."

"Okay, you have any ideas?" Sarah asked.

"As a matter of fact, yes. How about Mabel June?"

"Oh, I like it, Jack. It's terrible. Let's try it."

"Mabel June," I announced proudly.

Elton answered. "My pride and prejudice will only allow me to answer this guess one way."

"What does pride and prejudice have to do with it?" I asked. "Just tell me if we're right."

Elton grinned, the skinny shit. He was obviously having fun being "in the know."

"The answer to your first question, Jack, is: it has everything to do with it. And as for your guess being right—nope, sorry."

Sarah and I re-huddled again, but we didn't have much inspiration left in us. We finally settled for something like Madeline
Joan, but that never sounded right, and sure enough it wasn't. I
tried to loosen Elton's tongue with a few beers and some flattery,
but he held firm. And he continued to hold firm over many years
and many beers. He turned out to be quite a loyal partner for MJ.

chapter five

Over the next year we began to establish traditions of our own. Sunday night dinners together, evening walks through the neighborhood, trips to the ballpark to sit in the cheap seats, visits to Santa Clara University to listen to their guest speakers in politics, philosophy, theology, and literature and to attend gallery openings and concerts. We also did picnics. We went in all four directions of the compass and all elevations. From beach picnics in Santa Cruz to the top of Mount Diablo, from underneath the Golden Gate Bridge to the redwood forests of Henry Cowell Park. The "coincidence" picnic was to the vineyards of the Napa Valley.

We started that morning by picking some fresh radishes, cucumbers, carrots, and snow peas from MJ's garden, then we loaded up the trunk with a few blankets and cushions, and drove to Antonio's. Antonio did a good business in picnic lunches during the summer. He would pack antipasto, several types of fresh baked Italian breads, a few pasta salads, two or three varieties of cheeses, and assorted Italian meats like mortadella, salami, and spicy meatballs. MJ and I loved the meatballs on an Italian loaf, while Elton and Sarah usually piled meats and cheeses on focaccia or flatbread. Antonio would also pack a bottle of Chianti, wonderful Italian cheesecake, and something to stimulate the mind. Antonio was nothing if not poetic, and a picnic basket from him was not complete without his addition of a quote, poem or simple saying. We kept them in a special place at The Gatehouse. Some of our favorites had been:

You are searching the world for treasure
but the real treasure is yourself.

If you are tempted by bread you will find only bread.
What you seek for you become.

—Rumi

If you would win a man to your cause, first convince
him that you are his sincere friend. Therein is a drop of
honey that catches his heart, which, say what you will,
is the great high-road to his reason...

—Abraham Lincoln

Absurdity: A statement or belief manifestly inconsistent
with one's own opinion.

—Ambrose Bierce 1842-1914, author of
The Devil's Dictionary

Man can climb to the highest summits, but he cannot
dwell there long.

—George Bernard Shaw

We piled out in front of Antonio's that day and went inside. MJ had called him from home with our order and he came out from the back holding a wonderful wicker picnic basket with a shiny silver lid and polished wood handles. Inside the basket was all the food as well as silverware and china, cloth napkins, crystal salt and peppershakers, and a fine cut glass decanter holding olive oil spiced with basil, garlic and red pepper flakes. The first time I had seen the basket, he was showing it to a young couple and explaining all the features of it. After they left I had asked him why he put such expensive items in a picnic basket and if he wasn't afraid of it being stolen. He had smiled at me, something he did frequently it seemed when I asked him a question.

"I put fine napkins, crystal and real silverware in there because life is special, and a picnic is a way to celebrate it. In some things it is appropriate to just get by, but in most activities we should enjoy life to the fullest. We spend far too much time worrying about the future or regretting the past, and not nearly enough living with joy in the present. And I don't worry about the basket being stolen. I trust people and most are very honest. And if they aren't," he turned and gave me a wink, "the credit card imprint I get before they leave helps out a lot."

He put the basket on the counter in front of the four of us and opened it with a flourish.

"For today's picnic we have fine Italian meats, cheeses and breads. Antonio's antipasto we have left behind because today MJ's garden has produced for us a very special antipasto. Also, the Chianti need not make the trip because I am sure the Napa Valley will supply more than enough. However, you will not find cheese-cake there like Antonio's, so four pieces are included here. Of course, only the best of silver, china and crystal for my four friends."

He took the money, gave us our change, and smiled at me.

"And I need no credit card from you four. You are honest, and besides, I know where you live."

His eyes twinkled and he turned to go back to the kitchen.

"Antonio, what verse have you put in our basket today?" Sarah called out.

"Eat the food, sip some wine, lie back on your blankets, and then read it," he said turning back. "Sarah, will you read it so the others can hear? Then each of you speak what you feel for thirty seconds. No more. If you go longer than that, you will not be feeling, you will be thinking, analyzing, and filtering. Thirty seconds, straight from the heart and soul."

He turned and disappeared into the kitchen. All of us hesitated a bit as we pondered his last remark. Like students preparing for an upcoming test, we were already wondering how we would do in Antonio's quiz of the heart. Of course, Antonio had no legal power over us, and we didn't have to do what he had suggested. But we knew we would. Antonio always seemed to tap into deeper truths, seemingly engaging us on some kind of soul level.

We finally grabbed the basket, popped it into the trunk and headed for the wine country. We had several options as to our route. South through San Jose, then up and around; or east over the Hayward-San Mateo bridge, then over; or we could go the way we chose this time: Highway 101 north towards San Francisco, past Candlestick Park where the Giants were playing later that day, over the Golden Gate bridge to Marin county, catching Highway 37 to Highway 12 which connects Sonoma—the "Valley of the Moon"—with Napa. Whenever traffic wasn't an issue we would drive through the city. The bridges were fabulous, the water spectacular, and the skyline magnificent. And I loved seeing a big league ballpark. Just driving by Candlestick sent shivers down my spine, and I would wish I were good enough to be playing there.

The sun was shining brightly as we neared San Francisco, but the city itself lay quietly under a thick patch of fog. The tops of the buildings and the spans of the bridges had broken through the fog and sat as if suspended on top of the gray mist. Light from the sun's rays bounced across the fog and off the steel structures, illuminating them in a strange iridescent glow. We stopped and stared, marveling at the sight.

As we crossed the Golden Gate we could see Alcatraz to our right, and then San Quentin—California's most notorious maximum-security prison since Alcatraz closed—became visible at the base of the Richmond-San Rafael bridge. I shuddered as I thought of being locked up and unable to enjoy sights like today, to say nothing of family, friends, and lovers. Antonio's words about living each day to the fullest, about joy being such a critical part of life, came back to me. I resolved to focus on things that brought me joy each day, and to cherish the special times. I was aware even then that 75 hours of work a week probably didn't fall into the pure joy category, but I had yet to reconcile my ambitions, work ethic, and obsessive planning for the future with my inability sometimes to enjoy the now.

When we reached the Napa Valley, we headed straight for our favorite spot. As we pulled into the grand old winery we looked at the Roman Numerals MDCCCLXXXIX above the entrance. When you deciphered them it worked out to 1889, the year the winery was founded and, indeed, the year the Christian

Brothers had made this site the first winery in the Napa Valley. It was a glorious old building that stretched half the length of a football field and was several stories high. It had stars on the outside at regular intervals and at first we thought these were decorations. In fact, as we found out later, these were washers for the tie rods that connected on either side of the building to give it structural support through the middle. We climbed out of the car and unloaded the trunk. It was time for a picnic.

We settled down into the meadow on the hillside overlooking the Christian Brothers estate. Although there weren't any really good picnic areas on the grounds, we invariably chose a spot nearby so we could drop in on Brother Timothy, the Master Vintner for the Christian Brothers. Brother Timothy loved his work. He loved being out in the fields among the grapes, walking up and down the rows inspecting the crop, occasionally feeling, squeezing, or testing the fruit clusters. He loved the roses planted around the vineyards that attracted the local aphids and kept them from feasting on the grapevines, and the rich, green clover that attracted bees to pollinate the vines. He loved the crushing room where they crushed the grapes and began mixing the liquids to get the right proportions. And best of all, he loved the aging room, with its huge oak and stainless steel barrels and rich, ripe smells. He would wander through the barrels and vats, smelling and sipping and taking notes as his mixtures aged and fermented. The main product here wasn't wine anymore, as it was in the rest of the Napa Valley. It was brandies and liqueurs, and the Christian Brothers' brand was well known and thought of very highly.

The four of us had met Brother Timothy one day as we toured the facility. Elton especially, with his interest in Irish beer and brewing techniques, was highly interested in the process used to make the spirits, and hung on every word from Brother Timothy. Brother Timothy could sense this keen interest and took us on the "special" tour to many of his favorite spots. Following that visit we had an open invitation to stop in and see Brother Timothy, and did so at least a few times a year. On this day, we planned to eat and talk, then head over to the estate and find Brother Timothy.

We laid out the blankets in the warm sun and stretched away the kinks from the car ride. I was already hungry and in favor of eating right away, but our unspoken tradition had always been to lie out in the sun, enjoying the warmth and watching the clouds roll by as we called out what each formation looked like to us. Then we would take a walk, looking for wildflowers and deer, and breathing in the fresh air. This was a very different experience for me, as I had always equated the saying "stop and smell the flowers" with people who had way too much time on their hands. Being forced to slow down like this, I always found myself marveling at the beauty and intricacies of nature and all the life hopping, flying, running, and buzzing past.

By the time our walk was finished, I seemed to have twice the appetite. The heightened anticipation of waiting throughout the walk, the clean, fresh air, and the exercise put me in a special category of being hungry. The food always tasted so good that I swore each and every time that it was the best meal I had ever had. This time was no exception and I dug into the Italian meats and cheeses and the wonderful breads. MJ's antipasto was equally good and we sipped Chianti that we had picked up at the winery next door. The excellence of the food was heightened by the anticipation of Antonio's great cheesecake at the end. I loved his cheesecake, and I always got a piece and a half because Sarah could never finish the large slices. After making a most robust pig of myself, I lay back on the blanket with a contented sigh, laid my hands on my belly and smiled peacefully at the sky.

"Well, Jack, you look like a picture of contentment." Sarah was looking at me as though she'd never seen me relaxed before, a delighted smile on her face.

"I am, Sarah," I said. "I am. We should do this every day."

"But how would you live without your fourteen hour days at the office, and the requisite stress and ill health that go with it?"

Her voice had the light, airy tone of a good teacher, but what she said had a sting to it. Not the sting of someone trying to hurt another, but the sting of truth that your inner self recognizes and holds quickly to the light. Why, indeed, I asked myself, did I work the way I did, when this fellowship, natural beauty and slower pace flooded my being with such a sense of joy?

My other half—the half that pushed and clawed and was shooting for the top of the corporate ladder—had a quick answer. Because that's how you fulfill your ambitions, get security for later in life, become a somebody instead of just another faceless drone in the world. As I listened to this inner voice I knew even then it was missing something—heart, soul, spirit, whatever it was that I felt inside as I spent these days with my friends. But that side of me wasn't as well developed. And within a day or two of my realization that I needed more spirit nurturing activities, I would again get caught up in the mad dash of life in the 20th century, and especially in my corporation. Soon, my resolution to focus on the slower, inner life would slip away and I would again be driven by external factors and stresses.

All this pounded quickly through my head as I listened to Sarah trying to raise my awareness again. I knew I couldn't articulate all these thoughts aloud—or maybe I was just afraid to—so I did what I always did in these situations; I smiled, shrugged my shoulders gently, and looked back into the sky. Had I been perceptive enough, I would have seen Sarah's wry smile, a slight look of sorrow, and her own almost imperceptible shrug.

"Well, is it time for Antonio's saying?" MJ asked.

"Absolutely," said Elton. "I've been wondering what it is all day."

"All right, remember his instructions," Sarah said. "I'll read it and then everyone gets thirty seconds to say what pops into their head. Don't analyze and think about it, just say what you feel. Jack, you start."

"Oh, not me again. Why do I always have to start?" I whined.

Sarah laughed.

"Jack, you rarely start any of our activities. Now, get ready, here it comes."

She took out the envelope, opened it and pulled out a small blue card.

"All right, here goes." She read only four words: "**There are no coincidences.**"

Everyone's face creased momentarily as they digested the saying, then they looked at me.

"Jack, thirty seconds, what do you feel?" Sarah said. I was racking my brain trying to figure out something intelligent to say when Sarah spoke again.

"Jack, don't analyze," she scolded. "What is your gut reaction to this?" The prodding finally got to me and I just let it out.

"My gut feeling? My gut feeling is that it makes no sense. Of course there are coincidences. We bump into someone on the street we knew from high school and had been thinking about; our phone rings just when we get in the door; we find an article in the paper on Mazatlan just when we're thinking of taking a vacation to Mexico. Life is full of little coincidences; they happen every day."

I stopped to catch a breath. I realized I had been talking a bit too loud and abrupt. But that's what I was feeling.

Elton applauded. "Way to let your feelings out, Jack. I'll go next."

I relaxed and smiled a little inside at Elton's words. I loved the qualities he had of never judging people—especially me—and being quick to find the good in someone or some situation. He just as easily could have said I was being a bombastic jerk with my tone and attitude, and he would have been correct. Instead he picked out what I had done right—spoke straight from the gut with no filtering—and then diverted attention to himself. God bless him I thought, and turned my attention to him. He was dramatically clearing his throat and preparing to speak.

"Ladies and gentleman, I have clicked my timer watch to begin the thirty seconds I have to respond according to Antonio's instructions. I realize he was asking us not to exceed the thirty second limit and to speak straight from the heart—no analyzing, filtering, or logical syllogisms, just our feelings. Therefore, I will begin speaking with my feelings leading the way, and the analysis and filtering left behind. As I begin speaking, allow me to remind all of you that I am from Ireland, and therefore may have quite a different interpretation of the recently read saying than all of you from the great and new land of America. So, to begin..."

A beeping sound hit the air and Elton glanced at his watch.

"Well, I'm afraid my time is up." He swept his arm dramatically in a flourish towards Sarah and said, "Sarah, it is your time, I believe."

"My time," she protested and began to laugh.

"You didn't say anything, Elton," MJ said.

"Precisely," he said in a clipped English accent, paused and looked at MJ with a little smile.

"Oh all right," Sarah said and smiled also. "I'll give it a try. But that doesn't mean you're off the hook. We'll come back to you."

"Excellent, Sarah, good show. Now on with it," Elton said as MJ and I chuckled at his British accent.

"Well," Sarah started, "this is certainly an interesting concept. My instincts are that it's true. I feel as though there is a kind of web surrounding and crisscrossing the universe and that all the thoughts, actions, and circumstances are somehow connected."

I could see how deeply Sarah was lost in thought as she responded. Even though she was trying to give us her "thirty seconds of feeling," it was clear that this one had struck a chord deep. Her voice conveyed her feelings of intrigue, wonder, and even awe at the complexity of the short, and seemingly simple, statement.

"If they are, if things are interconnected," she continued, "if there is a grand design for the universe, then there are, in fact, no coincidences. The seemingly coincidental meeting, or book that is left on your seat, or sudden trip back east, all are part of a greater, grander plan than we know." She stopped and her eyes focused on us as she broke out of her reverie.

"MJ?" Sarah intoned.

MJ got the hint. "Wow! I was going to pretty much agree with Jack—although not so vehemently. I always felt that things did just pop up and I would call that a coincidence. But after listening to Sarah, my whole definition of a coincidence is in question. I mean, the four of us all being hired and then being sent to the same orientation; and only us, no one else in the room. The instructor being late so we could start talking and then skip for doughnuts. None of us having a place to stay. Finding the perfect house. I would have said those were all glorious coincidences. But looking at them together, it seems hard to believe it was just lucky breaks that brought us to each other. It does seem like we were meant to be a part of each other's lives."

Elton spoke up. "What you two are saying sounds like a predestination concept. Like the scripts for all of our lives have already been written and we're just actors and actresses saying our lines."

"No, I don't mean it like that," Sarah replied softly as she chewed on her lip. "I believe we have free will in all that we do. It's just that I feel the doors and windows that open in our lives are opening for a reason. We can choose to walk through them or not, but I don't think it's a coincidence when they open. It is part of a much grander scheme than that."

"Yes," Elton said, "I see where you're coming from. And if we look at those supposed coincidences as doors of opportunity and push, they just might open."

"Yes, exactly," Sarah said.

"Wait, wait," I objected. I wasn't sure why I objected, as I had nothing to say, but I must have felt the need to defend myself. I searched my brain for a valid objection. None appeared so I went ahead and tried a rather lame one.

"I don't suppose you have any proof of this, do you?"

All three of them looked at me as if I had just changed into an alien.

"Just kidding, just kidding," I backtracked. "I know this is the kind of stuff where you can't really have proof."

"Well, not in the sense you mean, Jack," Sarah said a bit testily. "There are no 'controlled experiments,' no five year studies with control groups, placebos, and a lot of statistical number crunching. The proof here is in the experience. Life as you live it—each and every day. And if you pay attention to it, if you really focus on every moment in the present, you may see a flickering pattern start to emerge. Then you must trust your inner self, listen to that voice deep down. It will be telling you that the pattern is your life, and if you follow it you will start the journey down your path. Jack's path will be the voice only he can hear, the path only he can take." She paused and looked at me before finishing. "If he so chooses."

"Wow," MJ said once more. "Sarah, you are smokin', sister."

Sarah's eyes blinked a few times and she seemed to return from whatever deep, dark reaches of her mind or soul she had been. She blushed a little and took a sip of wine. Occasionally, these rich, spiritual thoughts would flow from her almost as if they bubbled out like a spring. When she "came to," she usually was a bit self-conscious. She was never one to lecture and always let people around her express whatever opinions they wanted. She would normally take it all in, as if she was in a learning state, occasionally ask a question or two, but rarely bring out her opinion with such force. When she did, it was as if the conversation opened up a well inside her and what was there had to come out. And I had to admit, what came out usually caused me to think about ideas that I hadn't thought about before. I always felt as though I was being given a lesson, a lesson that was really a gift, for I never would have thought of it myself. I always imagined myself opening it, the packet of words and feelings, and placing it inside of myself. Like many special gifts, this one did not have to be used now. It was for me, and I knew as long as I held it inside, it could surface again when I understood it better—when my life was in a different phase, when that door was in front of me and needed Sarah's message to unlock it.

She is a remarkable woman, I thought in the car as we crossed the Golden Gate and made our way home. I wondered what it would take for her to see me as a remarkable man. I sighed and punched at the radio button pre-set for KSFO, the radio home of the San Francisco Giants. I missed and the tuner squirted to a pop station. The unmistakable harmony of the Beatles floated out:

>*You're gonna lose that girl*
>
>*Yes, Yes, you're gonna lose that girl*
>
>*You're gonna loooose that girl...*

I turned it off quickly. Great, that's just what I needed to hear. A real confidence booster. I hoped it was only a coincidence—no wait, not a coincidence. What was it that Sarah said, a coincidence really isn't a coincidence, it's a criss-crossing of the web of...Jeez, I didn't know. I adjusted the rear-view mirror and stole a peek at Sarah in the backseat. Eyes closed, head leaning against the window, a stray strand of hair lying on her cheek. I shook my head slowly. I didn't want to lose that girl.

"Now this is getting interesting," Sandor cut in. "Every good tale must have a love story. A romantic sub-plot. Excellent, Jack."

I wasn't sure if he was making fun of me. "I'm not making this up just to have a better story for you. This is what actually happened."

"I know," Sandor replied. "Makes it all the better, don't you think?"

I wasn't sure what to think. I needed to find out who this guy was and where the hell I was. He seemed to sense my thoughts.

"Let's keep moving, Jack, so we can finish and take care of your requests. Stay with the romantic piece. Good stuff going on there."

Living in the same house with Sarah was wonderful, of course. But we were only friends, just as MJ and Elton were my friends. I wanted to change that but I wasn't sure how. My natural shyness around women compounded with my fear of screwing up our perfect living situation at The Gatehouse led me to be very cautious. I looked for signs from Sarah, anything that would give support to my hope that she liked me in a more than friendly way. Two conversations stand out.

The Gatehouse had become a gathering place for friends and neighbors. I don't know if it was just that we were friendly and open, or that the house had a special energy. Probably both. But we often had folks drop by, especially on Friday and Saturday nights. One rainy Friday evening Elton was waving a magazine in front of the fireplace. The lights were low and the fire flickered patterns on the walls.

"Hey, what do you think about this?" he was saying. "This science magazine is asking about the future.

"'What will humans be like when we have made the next successful step in our evolution?'" he read.

All kinds of answers popped out as the discussion gained energy. Most were focused on the physical. Supposedly unneeded body parts, like the little toe and the appendix, gone; better filters to breathe the polluted air; ability to grow back critical appendages like teeth, hands, feet, and fingers ("Hair" shouted our already balding friend Steve); changes to fight the effects of gravity on our skin and frame; electro-magnetic cell rejuvenation to fight the effects of aging.

A few ideas were tossed out that had the science fiction reader's flavor to them. No body, just a big head with a massive brain; ability to communicate telepathically; ability to change our molecules to fit the environment ("So," MJ cut in, "at Dynamics' Board meetings then, we'd just have a roomful of snakes all trying to swallow each other"); ability to disappear and reappear wherever we wanted (Elton thought that would make it hard to have a good game of soccer). While we debated these and other ideas it dawned on me that Sarah hadn't said a thing. She was listening intently and seemed to be enjoying the conversation, but she hadn't volunteered her opinion. So I asked. She thought for a few seconds and then spoke.

"Well, I think the next step in our evolution will show two things. First, we will be much less judgmental, allowing and respecting diversity of thought, appearance, and belief. Second..."

"Wait," I interrupted, "more on that." A slight wrinkle appeared on her forehead and she bit her lip as she arranged the words in her mind before she spoke.

"As we evolve, I think we will begin to see that there is no one right answer to things. At least in so far as we can see here on earth. Maybe in a universal sense somewhere the final answers are clear, but here we do not know enough, nor can we explain all the mysteries in the world well enough to say that any of us, or any group of us, has all the answers. Our western doctors insist that their way is the only way, and other types of doctors are quacks. Yet we see Chinese herbalists healing people by the millions, Filipino healers laying their hands on patients and diagnosing, then healing them. Eastern Indian doctors practicing their 5,000-year-old Aryuvedic traditions and diagnosing through listening to our *three* pulses, and healing by bringing our doshas into balance through diet, exercise, internal cleansing and breathing.

"Our Native American shamans, aborigine healers, and African witch doctors all have proven records of healing sick people. And we could add in acupuncturists, chiropractors, and homeopathic doctors as well. All have something to add. And this is true of so many areas like education, religion and spirituality. When we are truly evolved we will not judge someone as wrong because they have different thoughts than our own, we will want to learn from them to continue our own education. We will celebrate our differences and our learning opportunities."

Sarah stopped, I think a bit embarrassed by how intense she had gotten. She studied us and decided to finish her other point before we began to question her too much.

"The second point is an off-shoot of the first. As we evolve we will have an extreme openness to learning—especially about ourselves, but also about the world. I suppose you could say we will begin to know how much we don't know and start to learn it."

The conversation continued from that point, but I was thinking of other things. Sarah's words had jarred me. I could think of so many incidents in my own life where fun and laughs were derived from poking fun at someone different than you, or worse, decisions were made to include or exclude based on those differences. As an Asian American I had felt that, especially in the post-World War II environment. And I also knew that I had been involved in my share of excluding others. Sarah was right. We were a profoundly judgmental society, and so many of us believed that only our group had the right answer. When you stopped and thought about it, you *knew* it was the wrong thing to do and you never felt very good about it later. But we did it to fit in, or win approval, or just because we didn't think before we spoke or acted.

The second conversation that stands out took place a few months later, during a similar gathering at The Gatehouse. The group was discussing relationships—all types: work, love, friends. Someone asked Sarah what she thought most people wanted out of a relationship. Others had conjectured about love, caring, and so forth. Sarah said something quite different.

"I think most people are looking for control and approval in a relationship. They want to either control the relationship so it is what they wish, or they are looking for approval, for someone to tell them they are right and good and okay. And sometimes both. When your motivations in a relationship, or in life, are to win approval, or gain control, you are coming from entirely the wrong place. In essence, you are lying to yourself and everyone else. You have real feelings under there and they could be allowed to come out. But if you sift all your thoughts, actions, and remarks through the filter of 'will this get me what I want,' or 'will this gain me approval from this person,' then you have locked up the real you inside."

She paused briefly, let her eyes wander to the ceiling, then continued.

"And what self-aware person wants a relationship with someone who has their real self locked away? Not many. Certainly not me. Only those who also have their real self locked away are likely to accept that situation. And that is a recipe for disaster. Either a gut-wrenching separation when one decides to break out of their pattern and the other can't or won't follow; or fifty years of numbness as you each keep the real you locked up."

We looked at her, digesting her remarks, but she had one more thing to say.

"So that is what I see people looking for in a relationship. What I don't see is people committed to a mutually beneficial relationship that is equal on each side and totally committed to the growth of **both** people individually, as well as the growth of the relationship."

She stopped for good then, and the conversation started to whir as the group picked up on her concepts and began to analyze them. I didn't hear much. This was when I knew that Sarah and I would not be going out any time soon, other than as friends. If I was to have any chance of having Sarah like me as more than a friend, it was clear I had a lot of work to do. Her words had cut into me deeply. In truth, I knew the instant she said it that I was a "filterer" of grand proportions. In fact, it was one of the things that was making my career go, and had gotten me such high marks in my MBA program. I could sense what others were thinking or reacting to, and would adjust my answers or study habits accordingly. There were times when I would be nagged by the thought that my integrity was weak, but there was always a corporate buddy to tell me that that is what business is all about. And that I was good at it, and would be crazy to waste my talent.

But listening to Sarah, I really wasn't worried about my job or school ethics. I was concerned about Sarah, and how to make her like me. A lot. As I said this in my head, I realized how absurd it sounded based on Sarah's comments.

How to make her like me.

Translation: what did I need to do and say so she would think I was the man of her dreams? Answer: not think the way I was thinking at that very moment, the way I always thought. Not filter myself for her approval, or anyone else's. This wasn't my normal date's requirements, like pay more attention, bring more flowers, watch less baseball. This was a macro requirement. Be more authentic, be more real, be you, the real you. ALL THE TIME.

As I thought about my chances of pulling this off, only one thought kept coming to my mind.

"Holy shit, Batman! I'm in trouble."

"That is a colorful phrase, Jack" Sandor said. "I do like your use of language."

"Well, you can thank Robin for that one. I just gave it a slight modification."

"Here's another saying," Sandor said. "Have you heard this one? *When the student is ready, the teacher will come.*"

"I must have heard that saying before, because it seems very familiar," I replied. "But I can't place where I heard it or from whom. I think it means that each of us will receive what we need as we are ready for it. Like guidance, a teacher, a book, a key relationship and so forth."

"Your understanding is good, Jack. Where I come from we have a slightly different version: *When the student is ready, the teacher will come...and sometimes when you're not ready we'll try to help you along.* Now..." Sandor started, but I saw my opening and jumped in.

"You know, Sandor," I began, "to really appreciate this saying that is different from where you come, I really should know where you come from. Don't you think?"

"Nice try, Jack. 'A' for effort. Now, as I was saying, let's move this story along and go to your promotion into management. Let's see if you were being 'helped along.'"

"You can't blame a guy for trying. Can you?"

"Some may, but I do not. Continue."

I took a breath.

It was 1976, and as the United States was enjoying its bicentennial I was making my push into management. The visibility of my negotiating teams as well as Ed's mentoring and sponsorship had put me in a prime position to take advantage of our company's expansion. The day I finally received my promotion, I was elated. I sat in my new chair, in my new office, and looked out the window proudly. The office was on the first floor, so I didn't have much of a view, but I gazed for a while at the few shrubs outside the window and the parking lot beyond. I phoned my parents, but they weren't home. What I really wanted to do was speed home and have a big celebration with MJ, Sarah, and Elton.

I had never been a big celebration person, but they were great at it and always made a big deal out of life's milestones and accomplishments. I would downplay celebrations concerning me and play a bit of the Scrooge. They would insist, of course, and off we'd go for a picnic, or to Father Antonio's restaurant, or just out to the backyard for barbecued burgers and an ale. Right now, alone in my office at the end of the biggest day of my career, I really wanted them to "drag" me out for a celebration.

But they were all gone.

Sarah had started medical school down in L.A.; Elton had been sent to our Washington, D.C. marketing office on a two-year rotational assignment; and MJ was traveling the country, "seeing America" as she called it, and trying to decide where she wanted to focus her life and her work. We'd had a glorious four years together, but in the last year everyone had gone. I missed them—especially now. I called Sarah's number, but she wasn't there. I tried Elton and got his message machine.

Now I was getting depressed. My big day, and not only was there nobody here to celebrate with, but I couldn't even reach them on the phone. I thought about just going home, but decided I'd learn from my friends and celebrate a grand occasion. Even if I had to do it alone. I packed up my briefcase and headed where I knew there would be a friend. Father Antonio's.

As I arrived, he was saying goodbye to a large party. He hugged the last member, waved out the door and turned to see me in the entryway.

"Jack, welcome. I haven't seen you in so long."

It was true. I didn't like to go out alone, and with the departures of Elton, MJ, and Sarah, I wasn't out much. And my 60 to 80 hour workweeks didn't leave much time either.

"I'm sorry about that, Father Antonio. I've meant to visit many times, but with work and such..."

"No need to apologize to me, Jack. And just call me Antonio, I'm not a 'Father' anymore. Come on in and tell me what has been going on in your life."

"Actually, Father—I mean, Antonio—today is a big day. I was promoted to management."

"Congratulations, Jack. That's wonderful, wonderful." He was beaming as if he were the one that had been promoted. "That calls for a celebration, don't you think? Come on in and sit down."

I was feeling better already, and happy that I had decided to come. As he led me towards the counter at the front where a handful of individual seats faced the grill, he suddenly stopped.

"Of course," he said. "I should have thought of that immediately."

"Thought of what?" I asked. But it was too late for words. He spun me around and steered me towards the back corner of the restaurant.

"Jack," he said as we arrived at a small booth, "do you remember Steve?"

Steve was sitting amidst a mess of typed pages with a red pen in his hand and one hand on his receding forehead, elbow leaning on the table. He looked tired and a little frustrated. And I did remember him. Elton had invited him to several of our get togethers at The Gatehouse. They had met at a squash tournament. Not too many folks played squash in our area, so it was hard for Elton to find courts or opponents. He had finally found a health club with a squash court, and in his first tournament he drew Steve in the opening round. Steve was a California native, but had spent several years in England and had learned squash. Elton had drubbed him in the tournament and felt so badly about it that he invited Steve over for a cool drink. A friendship ensued, and I always told Elton that he liked Steve because he was an automatic ego boost on the squash courts.

"Yes, of course, I remember him, Antonio. He was Elton's favorite whipping boy on the squash courts, and put away an ale or two at The Gatehouse." I turned to him and held out my hand smiling. "Hi, Steve, how are you."

"Fine, Jack. Still playing squash, and if I could get Elton back here, I believe I'd whip him good, now." He laughed; we both knew that was unlikely.

"Steve," Antonio explained, "Jack has just received his promotion into management and is here to celebrate. Can you take a break and celebrate with him?" He peered at Steve. "Actually, you look like you need a break, and maybe some special cheesecake."

Steve smiled and dropped his red pen. "I think maybe I have hit my frustration limit for the night. Sit down, Jack. Barkeep, a bottle of your best, cheap Chianti. Food for my friend! And cheesecake for me. Let's party!"

Antonio gave him an exaggerated bow and looked over at me.

"Lasagna?"

I nodded. He had remembered my favorite even after all these months.

"Excellent choice, as usual. And the first bottle of wine is on me. As congratulations to you, Jack, for your promotion, and to you, Steve, for tackling that subject for your Master's thesis." He turned and headed for the wine rack and returned with a short, round bottle of Chianti, the kind with the straw still wrapped around the bottle. He opened it with a flourish and poured us each a glass.

"Enjoy," he said, eyes twinkling as he performed another mock bow. "And may your discussions be fruitful."

I watched him as he moved across the room and settled at another table. I had seen that twinkle in his eyes before. That usually meant he was up to something. When his eyes twinkled, my eyes were about to be opened. I turned my attention to Steve.

He was scooping up his scattered pages and pushing them to the back of the table. One fanned out as the pile moved and slid into my lap. Although I wasn't trying to snoop, the phrases "Three Stooges" and "Management by Moe" caught my eye. As I handed the paper back, I couldn't help but smile.

"What did you see?" Steve asked.

"I'm sorry, I didn't mean to look at your work, but two phrases just jumped out at me. 'Three Stooges' and 'Management by Moe.'" I shook my head slowly and grinned. "I love the Three Stooges. Elton and I used to watch their re-runs three or four times a week right before bed and just howl. I think my eyes must be 'Stooge-sensitive' because without even trying to focus, that's what I saw."

"Don't be sorry," Steve said. "I'm not trying to keep this a secret."

"Well, if you don't mind my asking," I continued, "I thought Antonio said you were doing a Master's thesis. But the Stooges? And Management by Moe? How do they possibly fit into a thesis? Or did I just go to the wrong college?"

Steve smiled. "Well, if I remember right, you did go to the wrong college. You went to Cal, and any self-respecting Stanford boy like myself knows that is the wrong college. Notwithstanding that," he said as he waved off my attempts to protest, "I may be the one that is all wet this time. I am getting a Master's in Management and attempting to show that

Management by Moe," and he doinked me in the head gently but with full Stooges sound effects, "is the prevalent management style these days, and has to be changed. I am having a lot of fun writing about the Stooges—frankly, without that fun I'd probably never work on it, I am so tired of writing papers—but, trying to bring it all together is making my head hurt."

"I love the concept, Steve," I said, "but I'm still a little fuzzy on what 'Management by Moe' would be. I mean, how do you relate Stooge antics to an actual manager and what he or she does every day?"

He patted the pile of papers and sighed. "I have ideas on how to do that and sometimes I think this will be a lively, original, groundbreaking paper. But, other times—like now, for instance— I think I may have gone off the deep end." He looked up, then suddenly his face brightened. "I have a thought, Jack. I need to drop off a package at a friend's house. I was going to do it a bit later, but what if I did it now and left my thesis here? You could eat and read, and then, when I return, we could try the cheese-cake together and you could tell me what you think. I could sure use an objective viewpoint right about now. And as a new manag-er, you are part of my target audience." He paused but before I could say anything he spoke up again.

"I'm sorry, Jack. I'm so excited thinking about getting a fresh viewpoint on this that I forgot about you and your celebration. Forget what I said, let's celebrate your promotion and we'll do my thesis another time."

"No, no," I quickly cut in. "I like your idea. You've already eaten anyway, so do your errand and we'll celebrate during dessert. Remember, the celebration is about me being made a manager. What could be more appropriate than for me to read a great thesis on management before I start managing."

"I don't know about great," he said, "but if you really don't mind . . ."

Steve still looked a bit uncertain, but I reassured him, and soon I was alone. Truthfully, I really didn't mind reading it, and I

did like to read while I ate. Also, I was more than a little interested in its contents. My push to management had been a focused
and single-minded effort just to get there. I really hadn't given a
lot of thought as to what I would do once I was there. I didn't
have a management plan, or even a theory to which I subscribed.
I just figured lots of hard work would get me promoted, and once
promoted, more hard work would keep me moving up the chain.
So whatever I could learn here would be a bonus. I grabbed the
stack of papers and arranged them on my right as I always did
with my reading material when I ate. As if on cue, Antonio
showed up with my lasagna and placed it in front of me.

"Good eating, my friend . . . and good reading." His eyes
twinkled again and he was gone.

I paused in my story and thought about the thesis and how to
relate it in a story.

"Sandor, I think Steve's thesis is relevant to my story."

"I agree," he said quickly. "Would you read it please?"

I gave a broken laugh. "You're kidding right? I mean, I have a
good memory and all, but not that good."

"Oh, you'd be surprised. Just focus."

I was going to pop out a sarcastic little remark like "oh great,
how about a few more surprises" but I was afraid I'd get a few
more, so I just shut up and concentrated. And there it was. The
thesis. I saw it clearly in front of me. I was about to question
Sandor again, but a quick cost-benefit analysis told me I would
just be wasting time. So I began.

BEYOND MANAGEMENT BY MOE

*I was at a painting party. My group and I were painting a
home for troubled youths, and I was sporting my traditional paint
party shirt: black with a huge picture of Moe Howard of the 3
Stooges on the front. Above his picture in big letters it read "Moe
Knows." Next to his picture was a list of what Moe knew: Eye-*

Poking, Shin-Kicking, Head-Banging, Nose-Tweaking, Chest-Bumping, Hair-Pulling, Pie-Throwing, and Face-Slapping. Below Moe was a small picture of Moe, Curly, and Larry together, and the exclamation, "Moe, you do know diddley."

Obviously, this was one of my favorite shirts, and I thought the ever-increasing amount of paint decorating it merely gave it more character. I was painting a small laundry room with no ventilation and getting a little cross-eyed from the fumes. I stumbled outside where most of the group was gathered, and began to take abuse. Technically, I was their manager, but they knew the real power was with them (we'll talk about this later), and were not shy about unloading when I gave them an opening.

"Painted yourself pretty nice. Get any on the walls?"

"With those eyes, you ought to be over at the Substance Abuse Center."

"What took you so long, that was a teeny-weenie room."

"You know, with that haircut, you're beginning to look like Moe."

The mention of Moe brought me out of my stupor and I advanced on them menacingly, making "Stooge" sounds as I went. I brought my hand up in the traditional two-fingered eye-poking position and attacked the nearest confederate. He had seen the Stooges, apparently, because quick as a flash his hand went up between his eyes in the block position and thwarted my attack. I picked up an empty paper towel core and complete with sound effects of a hollow head being bonked with a hammer, bonked him. Soon "doink, doink," "oh, a wise guy, huh," "whoop, whoop, whoop, whoop," filled the air and Management by Moe was born.

During our annual summer "Western Days" celebration a few months later, a few of us did a "safety" skit where we led a group practice of the three ways to thwart a Management by Moe eye-poking attack— (for those of you who need it, the three ways are the traditional hand between the eyes, the last second head turn, and wearing thick glasses). The group hooted and I'm sure the "special invited guests" thought we were a bit daffy, but I suddenly felt there

was a story behind it all. We were laughing, but Management by
Moe was the prevalent management style in the fifties, sixties, and
early seventies, and in some places is still going strong today. Not
that we as managers and executives physically pulled hair and poked
eyes (at least most of us didn't), but we took dead aim on the spirit of
our employees. We didn't consciously say, "let's destroy some spirit
today," but we failed to recognize that spirit was the most critical
attribute for our organization to have. And we developed policies and
procedures, time-keeping systems, compensation practices, cubicle
requirements, dress codes and on and on until it was pretty clear that
we were Moe and they were the rest of the Stooges.

Spirit doesn't grow in this environment, and after a while only a
half or a quarter of each employee accompanies them to work, and the
rest waits in the car or cafeteria for recess. We talk about the energy or
power to leave your competitors behind, and it lies in the ¾ that is left
behind in such a spirit-zapping environment. Joseph Campbell says,
"follow your bliss," and most of us can't follow it at work. What if we
could be passionate about our work? What if all the people at your
company were passionate about their work? What about at home?
How many of us even know what our bliss is anymore?

MOE KNOWS—Eye-Poking

The stooge two-fingered eye-poke is one of the most famous of all
the stooge antics. When Moe (and it usually was Moe) delivered the
eye-poke, the recipient (usually Larry or Curly—although, of
course, Shemp, Joe, and Curly Joe were also Stooges) was blinded
and unable to proceed on his own. Moe would then have to "lead" the
vision-less stooge as he tried to accomplish his next goal. This concept
of leadership—"leading the blind"—is used by many organizations
as they practice Management By Moe. The idea that only the executives can provide vision is very prevalent. It's also very dangerous.
If the employees do not buy into the vision you have produced, you
will lose a great deal of spirit and trust in the workplace. The notion
that "you"—the executives, the big-shots, the "haves"—are planning
and executing strategies for your benefit at the expense of "us"—the

peons, the little-folks, the "have-nots"—will begin to spread around the work-sites. The workers will measure your words and your actions and if the two don't line up you will start to lose them. And later, when you need their understanding most—when that strike threatens, or the economy softens and lay-offs are necessary, or mandatory overtime is a must to meet commitments—when you most need them to say, "Yes, we understand, it is time to buckle down and work through this tough time," they won't be there for you. Instead, the mistrust, antagonism, and pent-up anger will emerge. They finally have some control. You need them to pull off your plans efficiently and effectively, and they know it. Now they will make you pay.

MOE KNOWS—Face-Slapping

Another famous Moe technique was the face slap. The slap degraded and humiliated the recipient. In Management By Moe, the slap takes many forms and can be directed at one person or the whole workforce. Here's one of my favorite examples from a large manufacturer.

A young manager sitting in one of his first management staff meetings listened as the senior executives bemoaned their low rate of production. Something had to be done to improve it. Finally, they zeroed in on the big issue. The manufacturing workplace at this time was predominantly men, and they were spending too much time in the bathroom. Management felt time spent at the urinal was reasonable, but that the men were spending too much time in the stalls. Furthermore, they had been sneaking things into the stalls to read!

Their solution to the problem was to take the doors off the stalls. This would make it very easy to spot transgressors, as well as encourage a speedy visit—for modesty if for no other reason. And, of course, the young manager (who had said nothing) received the job of removing the doors and "policing" the area afterwards to ensure compliance. He thought about it all week. He couldn't articulate the lack of respect and reverence being shown towards the men, but he knew it felt wrong in his heart.

At the meeting the following week, the executives wanted to know how the bathroom project had gone. The manager took a deep breath and began. He hadn't taken the doors down, he said, because it wasn't a cost-effective way to achieve results. You had the cost of removing the doors and transporting them somewhere, as well as storage costs or disposal costs. No, he said, he knew he had to find a better way. He then unveiled his meter maid "chalk stick."

"I'll tour through the bathrooms," he told them, "and reach under the stall door and mark each man's pant cuffs with chalk. When I make my return visit all those with a chalk mark will be busted."

Following a stunned silence and a few titters from the brave souls in the back, the executives agreed to drop the plan and encourage productivity in other ways.

I was chuckling aloud as I finished and Antonio arrived to take away my cleaned plate.

"So, do you like the thesis, Jack?"

"Yes, I do," I said looking up at him. "At least so far."

"What do you like about it?"

"Well, first off, it's fun to read, and usually a thesis is pretty boring. Second, I guess I see a lot of truth in it. I see examples around our company where we sure don't treat people very well. I suspect that isn't the best way to get people motivated to do a great job."

"You suspect right, Jack. As a manager now, you get a chance to treat people well...or not well. And as you manage more and more people over the years, your opportunity to make a difference will grow. This is a serious responsibility, and I know you take it seriously. And don't you think a happy, motivated set of employees will out-perform the others?" He smiled suddenly. "Ready for your cheesecake?"

I nodded dazedly, and he buzzed off. Antonio had a way of bringing up critical issues and making critical points, then smiling and leaving you to ponder them. I had never thought of the management of people as a responsibility I had to **them**, to treat them well, to care about their well-being. To get them motivated to do a good job, sure, but to actually care about them? And what about out-performing others? Isn't that what I wanted? To have a work group that out-performed all others?

I turned back to the thesis and finished it in short order. Steve returned about that time and we ate cheesecake and discussed his thesis. He was convinced that we needed to really pay attention to our employees and how we managed them. Management by Moe stood for anything that didn't respect and value the employee, and he had plenty of examples of that. As did I.

"When the student is ready, the teacher will come," I heard Sandor say. And then he added the addendum: *"...and sometimes when you're not ready we'll try to help you along.* Do you think you were ready, Jack?"

"No, I don't think I was ready, nor was I much of a student. When I read Steve's thesis I wasn't too sure about all the 'touchy-feely' stuff he wrote, but I could certainly see the difference between a caring, thoughtful manager and one who wants to form a 'stall Gestapo' to bust people for taking too long in the can. I actually did leave Antonio's that night determined to keep this in mind as I tackled my new job. But the next few weeks were crazy as I made the transition, and new requirements were arriving daily. Slowly the conversation faded, like a dream you meant to remember that just slips away."

"A dream is a very good analogy, Jack. It is there and it teaches but you must consciously try to remember it and act on it; otherwise it fades very rapidly."

Yes, I thought, it sure does.

chapter **seven**

"Jack, let's get back to the romantic subplot," Sandor said cheerfully. I think he enjoyed listening to stories of my ineptitude around Sarah.

"You're liking this way too much," I said. "I bet you're a dork around women yourself."

He laughed. "If you like we can talk about that later, too. You never know, I might be quite a ladies' man."

"Right," I snorted derisively. I thought maybe if I worked him up he might let some nugget of information slip. But no such luck.

"Move on now. Talk about that Sunday morning when you set up your visit to Sarah. Tell that story. And include The Gatehouse. It has always been a part of your story."

All right, I thought, here we go again.

I rolled out of bed that Sunday morning at dawn. I loved this time of the day and normally I didn't get a chance to enjoy it since I was in the office by 6:00 a.m. the other six days of the week. I grabbed the paper out of the driveway, and headed for the backyard with my cup of coffee. Climbing into the hammock, I set the coffee on the tall table Elton and I had rigged up to hold our ales. I gazed at The Gatehouse and felt a surge of happiness. I was so glad I had trusted my instincts and stayed there. MJ had been the last to leave, and after she started her tour of the United States my first thought about the house had been a business one:

Move out.

Without anyone to help with the rent, it made no business sense to stay. And, of course, I didn't need all that space. But from somewhere deep inside, my intuition was shouting at me: "Don't leave." I heard it over and over. So I didn't. I called our old friend and landlady, Barbara, and asked her for a break in the rent until I got a few more raises. She suggested new roommates, but I couldn't imagine anyone else digging in MJ's garden, relaxing in Elton's hammock, or soaking in Sarah's bath. So I scrimped for a while and hung on. And after things got a little better, I called Barbara back and told her never to sell the place until she talked to me. I didn't want to part with it. I thought about the memories that were so strong, and the joy in them. Nights by the fireplace, hot summer days around the hammock as Elton lounged in it and regaled us with stories of Ireland, and evenings on the porch, quietly swinging back and forth in the dusky air, a peaceful calm entering my body.

But even more than those memories, I was tied to the house by what each of my roommates had left behind. Their caring, compassion, feelings, joyous excitement, and pure energy of love had infused the house. I could feel the energy each time I entered, and it not only gave me a lift, it brought back the incredible insights my three dearest friends had given me. Their words of wisdom and their actions that modeled those words came to me strong in the house, and I knew I needed that. Ambitions and corporate ladders aside, I needed to be grounded and to reflect on the lessons of people and life that was my greatest gift from them.

It had been four years ago that MJ had left and I had made my decision to stay. And even though the majority of my hours were spent away from the house working or traveling, I always knew where I was coming home to, and that never failed to lift my spirits.

I sipped my coffee, unrolled the paper and pulled out the front page. It was summer and the temperature was perfect this early in the day. I read bits and pieces of the paper, but my mind was elsewhere—thinking of a business trip I was to take the week after the fourth of July. To Los Angeles. For once my mind wasn't on the business aspect. It was on Sarah.

She was in residency down there, and I was going to call her today and see if we could set up some time together. Of course, I knew she would be incredibly busy as a resident, but I was hoping for a bit of luck and a dinner date, perhaps even a visit to the theater to see the latest play. I reviewed my strategy for the visit.

I had carefully chosen today for the call. Two reasons for that. With ten days until I flew south, it was close enough that she should have a pretty good idea of her schedule already, yet it still gave her plenty of time to make arrangements in order to see me. The other reason was simpler. I had been afraid to call her when I found out about my trip two weeks earlier, so I made a plan instead. (First rule of business: If you don't know what to do, make a plan. Keeps you from having to actually do something.) Now, for me to be afraid to call Sarah sounds ridiculous, given that I had known her for over seven years—but this was not an ordinary visit.

First, even though it had been so long, most of our time together had been with a group. MJ, Elton, Sarah, and I had done most everything together during our years at The Gatehouse; and, with Sarah in L.A. now and very busy, our chances to see each other had been rare. And even those had been the result of a visit by her (which usually led to a group gathering), or myself and Elton or MJ, or both, heading down to see her. So what might be called a date—us alone and out together—was not a common occurrence.

Second, I thought I might have a chance with Sarah now.

My promotion to management three years earlier had been followed rapidly by other successes. I had been put in charge of several special teams that had been asked to fix key company problems—Dynamics called them "Tiger Teams." The visibility was great, and with each success my reputation grew, as did my access to the executives. I was on the verge of another promotion that would bring several more small organizations under me. My "empire" was being built, and by all standard measures, I was a success story. My confidence was starting to grow.

There **was** a nagging little voice in my head that advised me not to equate my professional growth with personal growth. But even though I sensed Sarah and I were still operating on different frequencies, I thought I had closed the gap. Sarah was well on her way to becoming a doctor, a profession of high prestige, big money, and long hours. That sounded like my profession, at least the one I was aspiring to—CEO of a major company. She would need a husband who understood her hours and her dedication to her work, someone who would have his own dedications and focus. That sounded like it could be me.

One other factor was key. I had been getting attention at work from several women, and one in particular. At first I had missed the signs, being focused as always on my career. But as I spent more time with them in a variety of work assignments, I started to recognize that their interest in me was more than professional. And Laura, the "one in particular," called frequently to discuss work, but always steered the conversation to personal topics. She suggested lunches to talk about our projects, and drinks after work. Even as blind as I was to these kinds of things, I knew she was interested in me.

My initial reaction to this interest was pretty typical to the human species. I was flattered. My confidence rose a notch, and I felt more attractive. Nothing had actually changed in my life, but someone else's interest made me feel validated in a sense. I developed a bit of a swagger, and as other women saw my confidence, I became more attractive to them. It was in this frame of mind that I began to think seriously about Sarah again. A big part of it was my confidence. The other part came when Laura invited me up to her family's cabin at Lake Tahoe. It was to be during Labor Day weekend, and Laura was smart enough to give me plenty of time to decide.

"Jack," she had said, "I know your schedule is hectic, especially with the Caulley Project and the attention it's getting from the President's office. But your deliverable for that is late August, and if everything goes as planned—and with you leading it, I know it will—then you'll need a break. No need to tell me anything now, let me know as soon as you see the light at the end of the tunnel."

Laura had punched all the right buttons in her invitation. A little flattery, work requirements understood, no pressure to decide now, and if plans were overcome by work, then work would take priority. Also, after pushing to the completion of a big project, I was always exhausted. Lake Tahoe was one of my favorite places, and the idea of spending time there in early September—one of the best times of the year there—was very appealing. I liked Laura, too. She was energetic, smart, and not bad to look at, either. Her rich, brown hair just clipped her shoulders, framing her slightly round face and a small nose that threatened to turn up. Rumor had it that she had once been thirty pounds heavier and very low on confidence—the victim of a few nasty "dumpings" by serious boyfriends. Not now. She carried her 5' 5" frame high, ran to keep in shape, and was known as a bulldog in the procurement department.

As I thought about the invitation and Laura's pleasant face, Sarah's replaced it.

I realized that she was the one with whom I wanted to go to Lake Tahoe, or anywhere else for that matter. I did like Laura, but Sarah had a special place in my heart. My feelings for her were strong, and I also admired her, respected her, and wanted to learn from her. Some may have called what I felt love, and it probably was—but I never said the words, not to anyone, or even myself. Not even under my breath, or in my head. That emotion was just too dangerous to let out. But the fact remained that Laura had asked me to spend a wonderful weekend with her, and I needed to make a decision.

My decision was to see Sarah and try to develop our relationship so that she might go with me on a special trip. Just the two of us.

I roused myself from the hammock and headed inside. A shower, some breakfast, and the last few sections of the paper would make it past 8:00 a.m. No more excuses then. It would be time to call.

"Hi, this is Sarah," I heard her voice say.

"Yes, this is Mr. Harrison from the IRS."

"The IRS?"

"Yes, and I need to see you very badly the week after next."

"The week after next..." she said weakly.

"Yes, on July 6th, about 5:00 p.m. I'll pick you up at your place..."

"Pick me up?" she interrupted, her voice starting to rise.

"...and after a cool drink on an outdoor terrace, we'll have an exquisite dinner, then off to see *A Chorus Line*, capped off by dessert and after-dinner drinks at Spago's. This is a full audit, Miss Sarah."

"Jack! That's you, isn't it? What a rotten thing to do. My parents had a horrible time with the IRS. You scared the dickens out of me."

"Well, it's about time someone got that Dicken's character out of you. He's old hat now. You must start reading some writers from this century, like Philip Roth and Truman Capote."

"Oh, Jack, you really are full of it today. And I do read writers from this century. Like Joan Didion, for instance, she's wonderful."

"Sorry, Sarah, no time for an author's review. What about the 6th? Can you spare a minute for your old buddy?" I was riding high on my wave of confidence and the words were just flowing out, sharp, quick, and—I thought—even a bit witty. I waited confidently—maybe even smugly—for my proposal to be accepted.

The line went dead for several seconds. When she replied, her voice had changed, dropping slightly, and becoming hesitant.

"The 6th? Yes, I think I can manage that. Call me next week and we can arrange the time and place more precisely."

"Sure," I forced out, "I'll call you next week. Bye, Sarah."

I set the phone down and lay back on the couch until I was staring at the ceiling. A big breath escaped me and my confidence floated away with it. Just a few little words from Sarah and I was back to square one. And she hadn't even said no! But the hesitation, the voice, even the words she had chosen had hit me like a rejection. I took a deep breath and tried to fill myself up with fresh air and fresh confidence. Ten days to get ready. Ten days to figure out how to tell Sarah some of the things I felt about her. Another deep breath and I felt a little better. With all her worries and pressures, of course she wasn't as lively and exuberant as I had hoped. Nothing to do but go to L.A. and let it out. Nothing ventured, nothing gained. Or, as they say in the golf world— never up, never in. I shook my head and laughed. Nothing like a few clichés when the situation was desperate. I pushed myself up off the couch and reached for the ceiling. My ten days started now. Time to get ready.

As the plane made its descent into L.A., I gazed out the window looking for UCLA and the nearby hospital where Sarah was doing her residency. I wasn't sure what I was looking for, never having been to UCLA before. I had, though, seen several shots of the campus on TV years before during UCLA basketball games. I had always enjoyed watching John Wooden, the "Wizard of Westwood" patrolling the sidelines as he won championship after championship with unbelievable players like Lew Alcindor, Bill Walton, Keith Wilkes, and Henry Bibby. Wooden stressed teamwork, discipline, and focus towards a common goal. I looked down again. I didn't see anything that looked like the UCLA campus to me, but as we neared the ground we passed right by the LA Forum where the Los Angeles Lakers played. They had drafted a very tall point guard from Michigan State named Earvin

"Magic" Johnson two years ago and he and Lew Alcindor (who was now known as Kareem Abdul Jabbar) had already lead them to a championship.

The plane thumped onto the tarmac and broke me out of my basketball daydream. I loved basketball, but could never make our high school team. I was athletic, but not really in a basketball way. As one of the young (and not so nice) assistant coaches had said, "Jack, what you lack in height, you make up for in slowness."

I rented a car and headed for my hotel. My watch said 2:30 p.m. Three hours until I met Sarah. I was going to hit the work-out room, pump a few weights, and in general try to get rid of some of this nervous energy. Then a shower, my best cologne, and a casual, but sharp—at least so said the sales woman at Macy's—outfit. Sarah and I hadn't discussed tonight in detail. I asked her to spare as much time as she could and to pick a nice spot for drinks and dinner, preferably outside on a verandah. I had found tickets to *A Chorus Line*, and I planned to use the tickets to entice her into making this a longer evening than normal, given her residency schedule. I pulled up in front of the hotel and turned the car off. The countdown continued.

I reached the restaurant first and secured an outside table. The sun burned hot even at 5:30, so I made sure to get one with an umbrella. I leaned back and watched the people passing by. It was certainly an L.A. kind of crowd, eclectic, absorbed, perhaps a bit younger here in Westwood than other parts of L.A. Lots of different fashion statements being made: old disco, new preppie, aging hippies and retro fifties. Very entertaining. I was having so much fun I didn't notice Sarah as she come up from behind and slipped into the chair next to me. She touched my arm as she spoke.

"There's no better show in town, Jack."

I jumped and turned to her.

"Sarah." She looked wonderful to me, although even in that brief glimpse I could see the tiredness in her eyes. We both leaned over to hug the other, but it was an awkward, chair style hug. I had planned to see her as she arrived and jump up and hug her with all my body and all the energy of my pent-up feelings. Instead, I looped an arm around her shoulder, tilted my torso and squeezed a bit. Not too satisfying. I leaned back into my chair.

"So, how are you Sarah, dear? You are looking wonderful, as usual."

She smiled. "Thank you, Jack. Even though I know that isn't true. I must look how I feel, and that certainly isn't wonderful."

"They working you to death at the hospital?" I asked. "Do I need to go down there and pull some rank, maybe kick a little doctor butt?"

She smiled again, but there was something else in her eyes. My mind started imagining what it could be and my stomach began to churn in response.

"No, Jack, that wouldn't help. There's something I know I have to do and I've been dreading it. I might as well tell you now instead of putting it off to the end of the night."

The sirens went off in my head and my stomach went into overdrive. Oh no, I thought, this is it. She heard my voice over the phone when I called to set up the visit, picked up on my intentions, and now she has to tell me there is no chance for the two of us. That is why she was hesitant on the phone. She is so sensitive and would never want to hurt me. She's been worrying about it for ten days, so of course she looks tired now, and has a strange look in her eye. She is about to crush someone she cares about—but cares about differently than I want.

My mind continued down that path and my stomach was crying for Maalox. Sarah was digging through her purse as I grabbed my water glass and took a swallow. She finally pulled out what looked like a letter.

"I'd like you to read this. I didn't know how to express it verbally. Every time I practiced in the mirror, it came out all wrong. So I wrote it down and tried to capture my true feelings about this." She paused and I tried to breathe. My heart had sunk until it felt like it was in my stomach too, turning end for end as its one true desire was yanked away from it. She handed me the letter.

"Jack, I want you to have some time alone with this letter."

I gulped and nodded.

"I'm going to my place to freshen up, I've been running around all day. I'll be back shortly. Would you please read my letter and tell me what you think? I need to send it out to my family very soon."

Her family? Send out my "Dear Jack" letter to her family? My heart stopped bouncing and sat up to listen. There was no good reason for her to send her family a letter about her and I not being a good match. Maybe this wasn't what I thought...

She stood, touched my arm and walked off. I tore open the letter.

Mom and Dad, July 5th, 1981

I am sitting here at home thinking about my future. You see, the one I thought I had is no longer. I have left my residency.

This is a hard letter for me to write. But, I guess I'm glad you're off traveling this summer, because I don't know if I could have done this in person. My emotions are so extreme now, and I am fighting tears and rage and melancholy.

I know you must be shocked and wondering what happened. But I am not afraid of your shock; I am afraid of your disappointment. Disappointment in me. Funny, but I thought I was over that. That I was a "big girl" now. But I do care what you think, and I do want you to be proud of me. I hope you will understand, and I hope someday you will be proud.

I've always wanted to be a doctor. You know that. What with Dad being a doctor, and Papa, and Aunt Marie, Aunt Jamie, and

Uncle Jarrod, it was in my blood. And I loved all our family get togethers where the talk always turned to the latest technologies, surgeries and medicines, and one after the other the family doctors told stories of their latest miracles. People brought back from the threshold of death, children given up for lost sitting up in bed and calling out for their parents. Tears of joy and gratitude at the unexpected reunions and lives and loves that were thought lost burning bright again. I was never happier as a child than listening to the stories and imagining myself healing those in need.

And I never doubted that I would be a doctor. I know you were a little unhappy when I went to Europe after college instead of going straight to medical school, and a bit concerned that I might stay when I went to work at Dynamics to save money for tuition. But I never had any doubts. It was a matter of when, not if, I would go to medical school. And when I started and graduated, and began internships and residencies, you were proud and I was on my path. So what happened? What did I see and feel that caused me to leave my residency?

My basic issue is this: I feel deeply that there is a distinct lack of love in western medicine. There is great technology and gadgets, but I don't feel much love. And how can you heal without love?

I thought for a long time about why this might be. What were the factors that had changed it from being a profession of love and healing—as I saw it being practiced by you, Dad—to one of technology, specialization, and treating the parts of a person instead of a whole person? Although I am reluctant to talk philosophy and concepts in such a deeply personal letter, I did do serious thinking about this and I want you to understand all the considerations that affected my decision.

Let's start with Descartes, the 17th century philosopher. Cartesian philosophy, as you both may remember, was a revolutionary combination of skepticism and mathematics that basically doubted everything but the doubter; thus his famous statement: "*Cogito, ergo sum*"—I think, therefore I am.

His continuing deductions from that led him to a very mechanistic view of the universe. The universe was not a live organism;

rather it was composed of non-vital atomistic matter. The way to understand it then was to reduce it to its simplest parts. Thus the term reductionism, and the tenet that the laws of mechanics were identical to those of nature. A good analogy was that nature was like a clock. If you took it apart and reduced it to small, simple pieces that were easy to understand, you could analyze those, and through understanding those, understand the whole.

Now, it is the environmentalists and ecologists who have the biggest gripe with Descartes on this, for his philosophy has promoted hundreds of years of thinking the earth is not alive, that we are not in partnership with it, and that we truly understand it as an overall ecosystem just because we understand some of the parts. And, of course, we don't and have many environmental problems to deal with because of it. But this is not my issue with Descartes.

My issue as a healer is that our western medical traditions have taken a page out of Cartesian philosophy and encouraged us to see the human body as a series of parts that, if understood, allow for the understanding of the whole. And this is clearly not true. We have begun treating parts, not people. Parts break and we fix them. Other parts break and we try to fix those, too. But I believe it is the whole person we must heal, and once healed, help him/her stay whole and healthy. This leads me to my second factor.

The second factor has to do with healing after the fact, not preventing prior. I said that I always wanted to be a healer, and that is true, but I now realize that I want to be a "preventer" even more. I want to understand the whole person well enough to help them not get sick in the first place. This is fundamental in many eastern healing traditions like Aryuvedic and Acupuncture, but lacking in western medicine. We are focused on treating the symptom, but not the cause. I was very discouraged during my internship and my year of residency as I watched, then participated in, the prescription of drugs, surgery and the like to mask or temporarily relieve what was clearly a symptom of a greater problem. When I questioned this, well-meaning doctors said they could only treat what they knew or could see— and they could see the symptom. They didn't have more precise knowledge, or the time to try and get it. Brings to mind the famous phrase, "Take two aspirin and call me in the morning."

As I watched this happening, my own stomach would hurt. At first I took Maalox and chalked it up to bad hospital food and lack of rest. Later, I looked underneath the symptoms, and that's when I left. I was actively participating in something I didn't believe in, and that was making my stomach hurt. Maalox covered it up, but to prevent it I needed to get away and be true to myself. But I learned a clear concept from this: emotional or even spiritual issues often cause physical symptoms. Another facet of treating the whole person.

Wait, I think I'm getting ahead of myself. Let's go back to the factors that caused my departure from my residency.

"First, do no harm." I believe this should be fundamental to our treatment of our patients. But often doctors are far too willing to anesthetize, cut, slice, stitch, and drug just to see if it works. The numbers of cesareans, hysterectomies, and even heart surgeries performed have been shown to be way too high for the benefit provided. Other much less invasive ways to help the patient have been shown to be just as effective, and far less traumatic. But also, and this leads me to my next point, far less lucrative.

Money, money, money, money. I found so much concern with money. Now, I am not saying the medical establishment is any greedier than the rest of our population, but I've always had the notion that healers are different. As I saw it, and as I witnessed in our family, healing was a lifelong passion. It was our bliss. It wasn't about money; it was about healing, saving lives, and living a life of service. Money might follow, but it didn't lead.

But what I saw contradicted my thoughts. Not only for the doctors, but the hospital administrators as well. In many instances, profit margins —both personal and for the corporation—determined the extent of care. Profitable surgeries for patients were encouraged, others not. Doctors were strongly encouraged to put enough people in the beds and on the surgery tables, or they fell out of favor. You can see how this ties in to the other factors. A $50 prevention visit didn't look too good dollar-wise compared with a $4,000 surgery.

But it isn't all doctors and administrators. Part of the reason money is such a big issue nowadays is they need to pay a huge cost for malpractice insurance. Our lawsuit-happy society has boxed the medical establishment in a bit of a corner. If they make a mistake they can be hurt badly, both financially and professionally. And maybe in certain cases that is appropriate. But they can also follow proper procedures that work 999 times out of a thousand, and get sued for the one that is an anomaly. So what's left? Order extra tests for the other 999 and raise everyone's insurance and hospital rates. In the name of "thorough treatment" cut, excise, drug or sterilize anything that could ever be a danger. "First, do no harm" is replaced by: "First, cover your backside." I can't say I have the answer to this one, yet. This is one area where we are all to blame, and we all need to help if we are to bring some reason to this insanity.

One final reason and I will stop. It was probably the last straw for me. The "medical establishment," made up of the allopathic doctors, hospitals, clinics, administrators, drug companies and the American Medical Association are very, very close-minded. Any "alternative" treatment is seen as a threat, not as a possible way to cure or prevent illness or injury. Somehow they are impervious to thousands of years of healing and prevention from China, India, Japan, the Philippines, South America and on and on. Entire cultures and traditions of healing are ignored because they're different and (here we're back to Descartes I'm afraid), the "establishment" doesn't understand how all the parts work, so they disregard the whole as well.

I've seen western doctors witness healing through energy transfer as in the Philippine tradition, (or the Biblical laying on of hands), or acupuncture, or Chinese herbs, or internal cleansing, and dismiss it as coincidental healing just because they didn't understand how it could heal. This lack of willingness to learn, and the extreme close-mindedness really convinced me that to follow my calling as a healer, to be able to try whatever it might take to prevent or heal illness or injury, I needed to be in an open, supportive environment where all possibilities - including western medicine - could be seen as legitimate alternatives.

Now I need to find and nourish that environment.

Many folks here urged me to re-consider my decision and finish residency, then try to change the system from within. But I know—deep down in my blood and marrow—that I must look elsewhere.

You know I love you both, and I am so happy to have been raised by the two of you. And the way our family practiced medicine has always been an inspiration to me. I hope you understand why I have to do what I am doing—and why I had to make this decision on my own. It has been difficult, but necessary. I must find my own path.

Love,

Sarah

P.S. To be fair to Descartes, I must say that I don't think he would have viewed people as he viewed nature. But the concepts and theories he began have carried forward—in dangerous ways—in many areas.

I tossed the letter on the table, exhaled loudly, stood up and stretched, then sat back down quickly. My body seemed to be following my mind, uncertain what to do and not sure whether to be worried, happy, sad, or scared. Nervous energy poured out of me and I really wanted to take a long walk through the tree-lined streets and sort out my feelings. Of course, I couldn't, not with Sarah coming back soon, so I hailed the waiter and ordered a beer. When it came, I took a long pull, sucked in several deep breaths and tried to relax and open my mind. So what was I really feeling about this bombshell?

Astonishment and disbelief were the first clear thoughts that had come to me. How could she throw away all those years of education? She had worked so hard and so long, and was so close to her goal. Everything had been set up for her. Her future was just beginning, and it was bright and full of promise, like a sea captain with a great ship embarking on the voyage of a lifetime. Now, it was as if Sarah was wading into a murky pond with no idea what lurked beneath the surface. It was inconceivable to me that she would just turn her back on the future she had planned, and for which she had worked so hard. One thought was clear to me. *I would never do that.*

And as that thought sank in, I felt my own ship starting to sink. Just as I had realized when we all lived at The Gatehouse, I saw again that Sarah was far beyond me. She was doing things for love, caring, healing, and I was thinking of power, achievement, and prestige—not to mention money. Of course, that was one big reason I was so attracted to her. She embodied principles that I admired and aspired towards. I often wondered how she got so wise; she seemed to have been born with special knowledge and wisdom. I knew I could learn from her. And more than that, I wanted to be with her. Desperately. I had waited long enough to decide to take this chance. Beyond me or not, I needed to make my play for Sarah. So what could I give her? What were my fine qualities?

I thought of Laura. I knew Laura thought I had some good points. I laughed out loud as I thought about calling her to ask.

"Hi, Laura, it's me, Jack. Just a quick question. What are my good qualities that make you like me so much? Could you give them to me now on the phone? I'm waiting for someone here that I'm really crazy about, and I'll need all the help I can get so she'll fall for me tonight. And, by the way, can I put you down as a reference in case she wants to verify it?"

"Jack, kiss my..."

I stopped my fantasy dialogue quickly before Laura really got going. I tried to list my good points: smart, hard working, loyal, conscientious, and a fast learner. And not all that bad looking, reasonably fit, okay dresser. That wasn't so bad. I wasn't ready to give up on Sarah and me so quickly, as I had a few years earlier. Maybe Sarah and I would be a good pair, good at learning and growing together. There was clearly something between us. After all, she had chosen me to read her letter first. That was something. She could have sent it to anyone, or given it to her friends here. In the back of my mind, I knew the timing of my trip probably had something to do with her decision to give it to me, but she could have sent it without my opinion. Yes, there was enough here for me to press on with my plan.

Or perhaps this new situation had opened up some different possibilities.

One ramification of her current decision was that she would need an inexpensive place to live, and probably would want to be away from her family so she could think and decide her future in private. Also, knowing Sarah, she would want a place that she really loved, a place that was special to her. Maybe with an incredible claw-footed bathtub and a hammock in the backyard?

As I built this scenario in my mind, I started to get excited. This might work. Instead of "going for it" that night and opening up with my feelings, I could invite her to move back to The Gatehouse. The rent would be cheap, her room was waiting for her, and I traveled a lot so she would have plenty of privacy. The benefits to her were obvious and plentiful. And the benefits to me were just as obvious and plentiful.

With no one else there but us two, I could begin to cultivate the relationship privately and steadily until I knew the time was right to fully open up to her. I could be a good listener for her, and a sounding board. She wouldn't have to worry about food or transportation. We could have picnics and take walks. A final benefit was that I would not have to own up to my feelings today; I could delay my true moment of reckoning. And when you were as scared as I was that the answer might not be the one desired, the hope of the future was preferable to the truth of today.

I took a deep breath and glanced down the street. There was Sarah, crossing the street a block down. Time to make a decision. Should I follow the old cliché...

There's no time like the present

or my modified version,

There's no time like the present unless the future is a better present.

Sarah made her way through the tables and I stood and held out my hands to her. She took them in her own and looked up at me.

"Sarah, I am very proud that you are my friend. Sometimes 'normal' people, including me, think of honor and principles and truth—especially our own truth and what we feel deep down is real truth—but usually we don't act on that truth. It often seems that truth goes against what our culture, or society, or our families and friends believe we should do. And usually we follow instead of lead. I'm pretty good at leading others at work, but not so good at leading myself.

"My first reaction to your letter was that you were crazy, that you were throwing away a great career, security, prestige and all that you had worked so hard for. But as I thought about it, I realized you can't separate your principles from your life, and you were willing to act on your convictions. That takes a kind of courage most of us don't have, Sarah. I believe you are just a bit further down the evolutionary path than most of us."

I stopped, out of breath and surprised by what I had said. I hadn't planned to say all that, it had just started flowing out. I felt a blush creeping up my face and Sarah had her own redness emerging.

"Jack, that is one of the sweetest things anyone has ever said to me. Most of it isn't true, especially the evolved part. But it is so nice of you to say those things, especially now with this whole decision weighing on me as it is."

We both sat down and Sarah looked over at my near empty beer stein.

"Started without me, I see."

I shrugged and signaled the waiter. "After reading that letter, there seemed to be no choice."

She punched me on the arm. "It wasn't that bad, Jack."

"It wasn't bad at all," I said laughing and rubbing my arm. "But, you have to admit, it isn't your ordinary letter. Even if it wasn't so monumental because of your decision, just the Cartesian philosophy stuff could drive a man to drink."

She smiled but her nose wrinkled. "Do you think that's too philosophical to put in a letter like this? To parents?"

"I don't know. I wouldn't put it in a letter to my parents, but your parents are different and your relationship is different."

"I really wanted them to know my thinking and what had influenced my decision." She stopped as her beer arrived. She took a slow sip and her eyes rolled back and forth as she searched for the right words. "But I don't want it to be sterile or unfeeling."

"Well, I don't know whether you should change it or not," I said, "but it certainly isn't sterile or unfeeling. It is full of passion and deep feelings. It's full of you, Sarah."

She started to say something, then stopped, picked up her glass, and nodded.

"Thank you, Jack. For taking the time to read it, and for the kind words. I'll give it a little more thought and editing, then send it out."

I saw my opening and jumped in.

"Then what? What are your next steps to find your path?"

She sighed. "I'm not so sure. As I said in the letter, I know healing—and 'preventing'—are in my blood. But I don't have a plan yet for how to get where I should be. Heck, I don't even know where that is. My mind is so full and my emotions at such a fever pitch that I can't think clearly now. I need to get out of this environment, rest a bit, then start researching and talking to the right people about the possibilities."

I began to get excited. This was perfect.

"Well, Sarah dear, have I got a deal for you. It just so happens that I have a big house that needs company, and a lonely claw-footed bathtub that wants to have nice bubble baths again. And a library close by, and a man who knows everyone, named Father Antonio, who can help you find the right connections and serve you great lasagna as part of the deal. What do you say? Move back in, same rent as before, and take your time deciding. And with me working all the time, you'll have plenty of privacy." I was out of breath so I stopped for air.

Sarah hesitated as she processed the offer, but I could see the light in her eyes and my hopes grew.

"That's very tempting, Jack. But that's your house now. I don't want to impose."

"No imposition. I would love it," I said truthfully.

She smiled wistfully. "I do love that house. And that tub. And Father Antonio." Her smile disappeared and my heart jumped. "But not at the old rent. I should pay half with only two of us."

My heart relaxed again. "Make it a third and cook up a batch of your Nana's navy beans and ham hocks once a month and it's a deal." I held out my hand.

She held hers out part way. "I pay half the utilities then..."

"Half the electricity and phone," I interjected. "I'll keep water and garbage." I reached out farther toward her hand, thinking all the while about what a crazy negotiation this was turning into. First time I'd ever negotiated for less money. But it felt right, and as our hands lay suspended over the table, Sarah finally nodded.

"Okay," she said and her hand bridged the gap. "It's a deal."

Oh my God, I thought to myself, this may be the best I have ever felt.

My hand was tingling, my heart was racing, and tickets for *A Chorus Line* were burning a hole in my shirt pocket. This was the time to bring them out as part of the celebration. Our hands parted and I reached for my shirt. Sarah stood at the same time and placed her napkin on the table.

"This is great, Jack. Thank you so much for offering. I am looking forward to spending more time at The Gatehouse. But first, will you excuse me? I must visit the ladies room. I think that beer went right through me."

"Of course." I stood as she departed, then sat back down. As I did I noticed someone jaywalking across the street and looking my way. I looked away, but when I glanced back he was on the sidewalk about thirty feet away peering through the crowd—with extra long pauses on me it seemed. He looked Hispanic, with dark hair pulled back in a neat ponytail and wore what appeared to be hospital attire. He was tall—maybe 6'2" or 6'3"—and, for a guy, had a nice looking face. But why did he keep staring my way?

A minute or two later when I looked up again, he was still there. And searching again, but still focused in my direction. Then suddenly his face changed and the searching, confused look became a happy, knowing one. He waved. I didn't think he could be waving at me, but it sure looked like it. He waved again and my hand started to creep up to wave back. Maybe he was just friendly. With that he stepped over the railing that separated the cafe from the sidewalk and started towards me. My confusion had just about reached an apex when I heard Sarah behind me.

"Raoul! How nice. Come on over and meet Jack."

Raoul reached us and shook my hand as I stood. "Pleased to meet you, Jack," he said with a smooth Spanish accent. "Sarah has told me so much about you."

"The pleasure is mine," I said. "Judging from your outfit, you must be one of Sarah's medical school friends." I hoped I was right and Sarah had only befriended a struggling young student, helped him with his studies, and politely invited him to a few group social affairs.

He leaned down and kissed her and my heart—just like in an old fairy tale—turned to stone. Maybe, I prayed, that was just a friendly custom from his native country. But as his hand continued to rub her neck and shoulders after he sat, it became clear. Sarah *was* meeting her special someone tonight. But his name was Raoul, not Jack.

She began explaining to me that Raoul was from Spain and in his first year of residency and so on. I wasn't listening. I had to get out of there. I stood up.

"Excuse me, I think it's my time to use the restroom now," I said stiffly and started walking. My tongue felt thick and my cheeks were hot. I got to the bathroom and began splashing cold water on my face. Finally, I dried off and tilted my face to the mirror.

I looked like hell. My eyes were already red and I fought to keep the tears from spilling over. I needed an excuse to leave somewhat gracefully, and then to be able to hold it together for a few minutes while I said my goodbyes. I thought a bit, took a deep breath and headed out.

Sarah and Raoul were in a lively discussion when I broke in. "I'm so sorry, Sarah. I phoned back to my hotel and the executives have called a dinner meeting tonight to iron out some problems with the proposal. I've got to go."

Sarah began to protest but I didn't slow down. I only had so many words in me.

"So nice to meet you Raoul, and we'll talk soon, Sarah. Oh, and perhaps you can use these." I threw the tickets on the table. "Someone gave them to me today. Have a good time."

I bent and gave Sarah a quick squeeze on her shoulder, shook Raoul's hand, and was gone. I ignored the calls from behind me and moved quickly onto the sidewalk. My eyes lost the liquid battle, and as the tears slipped out, I bumped and bounced my way down the street through the crowd, apologizing but never stopping until I reached my car. Once in, I laid my seat back, covered my eyes with my arms and cried. I knew now what I had always suspected. First, I truly loved Sarah. Second, I was not to be her man.

On the plane ride home, I made two decisions. One revolved around Sarah moving in. I had already kicked myself many times for inviting her to move in before I found out about possible romantic relationships. Now I had to fix the problem. I knew there was no way I could live with Sarah now. It would be too painful seeing her everyday and knowing we couldn't be together. Not to mention how I would feel when Raoul came up for a visit. So I made a decision. Run...

Not that I thought of myself as someone who would run from problems, but in this case, running was clearly the best alternative. At work, big challenges were my specialty. But big emotional challenges? I didn't think I was ready for those, especially this one. A word filtered into the back of my brain—coward. I shook it off. I knew I didn't have the emotional strength to deal with this. It was wise to run when you knew you couldn't slay the dragon—and I knew this dragon would scorch me in an instant.

I decided to accept a remote assignment in Hawaii.

The job was to set up a consortium of companies from several Pacific Rim countries to undertake a small joint venture and explore the possibility of future strategic partnerships. Highly experimental in both organization and objectives, the project had been offered to me by the VP a week earlier. I told him I would look at the details of the job, relocation, and compensation packages and get back to him in a week.

I had quickly examined those aspects, then talked to my political connections in the company. They told me it was a good job, possibly a great one, but it had the potential to blow up in my face. There was a good chance of failure with all the different nations and cultures colliding. Also, other similar joint ventures were being started around the world. If any of those proved successful first, then the glory—and the promotions—would go there. Bottom line—big risk that was unnecessary for me to take at this time. Their advice: express interest to the VP, but beg off due to personal reasons like upcoming surgery or illness in the family. Then, wait for one of the better jobs they saw coming down the line in the next year.

I was all set to follow their guidance when Sarah and Raoul jumped into the picture. Now, getting out was all that mattered and a job in Hawaii certainly did that. The morning after the plane landed I went to see the VP and accepted the assignment. I was to start right after Labor Day.

Then I went back to my office and picked up my phone to act on my second decision.

"Hello, this is Jack. I have good news. First, I've been offered the Program Manager position for the joint venture project in Hawaii. Second, I don't have to start until after Labor Day, so I'm free to spend the weekend at your cabin in Lake Tahoe. Is the offer still good?"

"Of course, Jack," Laura answered. "We'll have a ball. Let's work out the details over dinner. And congratulations on the new job. You deserve it."

"Thanks, Laura, and dinner sounds great. Meet me at my office at 6:30. Bye."

I hung up and let out a deep breath. Life was changing and I wasn't sure I was ready for it. But it was time to try.

chapter eight

"So your trip to L.A. did not go as you had hoped?" Sandor said.

"No, it didn't," I sighed.

"So you went to Lake Tahoe and then off to Hawaii?"

"Right."

"How was Lake Tahoe? Your decision sounded impulsive for you."

"It definitely was, but her offer intrigued me. First, I had never taken a real vacation. Usually when I took time off I just stayed at home with a pile of work from the office and waited for the inevitable 'emergency' calls from the boss. The few times I did get away it was to family functions—reunions, weddings, that sort of thing—and they were crowded and not very restful. So a true vacation sounded good. And I love Tahoe and the mountains that time of year. But I wasn't sure about going. I'm not all that slick with women in general and with Laura…" I groped for the words. "I mean I liked her and all, but we hadn't dated that much. And a long weekend…alone? Yeah, that was clearly impulsive. No doubt a rebound shot from my failure with Sarah."

"I am sure you are right. So was Tahoe a disaster?"

"Actually, no. It was very nice. Some hiking, some live music at night, relaxing dinners, and always the beautiful views. Oh, and did I mention the sex?"

"No, that must have slipped your mind. Was that important?"

I thought the question odd. Important? Incredible, exciting, sexy, mind-blowing—these were adjectives I related to sex. But important?

Sandor must have been listening in again. "Sex is wonderful in many ways, but it can be very important as a connection between people. The touch of another is something we all need."

"Gee," I said, "that doesn't make sex sound dirty and nasty and forbidden at all."

"And indeed it isn't," he said. "Unless you make it so. So back to my question. Was it an important experience?"

I thought about it, but only briefly. "Absolutely. When she touched me, when she came up behind me and wrapped her arms around me and laid her head on my shoulder, when I lay against her and let my head rest on her body, when in the half sleep of the night her arm dropped over me and pulled us together— those feelings were different than any I had had in a while. Touch is a good word. I felt my 'touch reservoir' start to fill, and I realized how empty it had been. For the first time I recognized how much I needed that. It felt great, and I wanted more touching— and I wanted the sex to keep going, too."

"What happened when you returned to The Gatehouse?"

"It was definitely traumatic seeing Sarah's stuff lying around. A few weeks earlier she had moved in, but then had headed off to visit her family on the east coast and tour Newfoundland. So I hadn't had to face her on a daily basis and I knew I needed to keep it that way. Laura had helped me forget temporarily, but seeing Sarah's bathrobe and a few of her favorite books lying on her bed had stopped my breathing and tightened my stomach. I knew I needed time to get over her, and seeing her—and maybe Raoul— was not going to help. I finished my preparations and was off to Hawaii within the week."

I chuckled.

"What's funny?" Sandor asked.

"Out of all this pain and confusion, the one area that prospered was work. The executives had taken my commitment to the difficult Hawaii job and quick departure as evidence of my loyalty and dedication. They were falling all over themselves patting me on the back."

"Have you noticed that you always had clear goals and dreams of being successful at work, of being a CEO—and this part of your life always prospered? This is not a coincidence."

I thought about the truth in that. Certainly for me it had held true.

"So what happened with Laura? You were about to go off to Hawaii now, right?"

"Yes. Laura and I talked on the drive home and agreed to see each other as much as made sense given the geography. She had always wanted to see Hawaii, so she was excited to visit me there and tour the islands. And, of course, I would have some trips back to Headquarters so that was a few more times together. I really thought it was a perfect plan. With my assignment likely to take at least a few years, this would give me plenty of time to figure out what to do."

"But," Sandor began, "something happened."

"Yes, again. Initially, my core team of managers flew out with me and we scouted locations, talked to our partners and made some customer contacts. I reviewed the draft operating plans of my departments and also their staffing plans. I was having a good meeting with my business manager when he slid his organization chart to the middle of the table. And there, as the procurement lead…"

"Was Laura," Sandor finished.

I nodded. "Exactly."

"So what were you thinking? Were you just scared, or did you see this as an opportunity?"

"Both, I think. I was very ambivalent. On the one hand, I realized in Tahoe how great it felt to be connected intimately to another person. But on the other hand, I was scared. The depth of my desire scared me. If you want something that bad, then you can make bad decisions trying to get it. I wasn't sure if what I was feeling was love—or need. Or some combination. And if a combination, what is the combination that is okay? Is 20% love and 80% need okay to make lifetime decisions on? Or should it be 80/20 the other way? Or just 100% love? I didn't know. I really would have preferred some time to sort it out, study it a bit."

"You are consistent, Jack," Sandor chuckled, then paused. "So tell me about Talk Radio."

I felt that blush of sheepishness pass over me, like when you get caught watching the soaps or leafing through a lingerie catalog. There's nothing really wrong with what you're doing, but inside you still feel caught.

"Talk Radio? You want to hear about that?"

"Yes and what led up to it. You're returning from Ireland and Elton's wedding and then…"

"Talk Radio, huh? You're sure that story is important?"

"Yeesss." He drew it out like someone who is patient but soon won't be.

"All right, all right. Just give me a minute."

"And reach down a bit. Let the true story and your deep feelings come out."

"Okay," I said. I tried to relax and focus. "Here goes.

Elton's wedding in Ireland had been fantastic. And so much fun. He had met Maire eighteen months earlier at his parents' 35th wedding anniversary. Or, actually, re-met her—for he had known her in childhood, had a little crush on her, then lost track with his exchange student activities and many travels. They had reconnected in a strong way and traded letters for a year before she had moved to the states for a more intensive trial. Elton had been worried about being apart for that year, but besides the logistical problems with both of them having jobs and commitments, Maire thought it a good idea. She had told him that some time getting to know each other through writing would be a good thing. She was very honest and straightforward. She said getting to know one another slowly without all the big decisions like "should we have sex?" "should we live together?" "should we spend all our time together?" and "do we like each other's friends?" complicating matters appealed to her. Smart lady.

So as I said, the wedding was great. Held at a castle and truly magnificent. But on the plane ride home I was envious. Plain and simple. Envious of Elton and Maire. And wishing that I had been the one with the storybook relationship culminated by a wonderful wedding. A wonderful wedding that included Sarah walking down the aisle with me. Seeing her again for several days in Ireland had reminded me of why I had fallen so hard for her and left me wondering if I would ever experience that type of deep, devoted, passionate, and spontaneous love. The highlight was a dance we shared. I was staring at the magnificent wedding cake and fantasizing that it was for Sarah and me. As others crowded around to look at the cake, I began backing up to let them in, all the while trying to keep it in view.

A voice in my ear shocked me. "Careful fella, you don't have your back-up lights on."

I jumped and turned and saw Sarah smiling, head cocked, a ray of sun from the window highlighting her hair. She was so beautiful I couldn't speak. I was staring dumbly at her when Elton danced by, MJ spinning with him.

"Come on, you two, get a little exercise," Elton shouted.

Sarah and I looked at each other for a few seconds. I put my hand out. She took it and...the song ended. I looked at her awkwardly.

"Hey," she said putting her other hand on my shoulder, "the band's bound to play another."

The music started almost instantly but instead of the fast jigs and reels that the Irish musicians had been playing, this was a slow song, a beautiful Irish ballad. We moved closer and began turning to the music. It was heaven. Her touch, her fragrant hair and soft shoulders, the simple swaying in unison—I could have gone on forever. When it ended, the spell broke. I felt awkward again and wondered what to do. Dance again, ask her outside for some air, or perhaps a glass of champagne? Elton saved me this time. Taking the stage he grabbed the microphone.

"Mike Scott," he said pointing to the singer and leading the crowd in cheers. "The song was *When ye go away* and it was brilliant. I just want to say to my lovely bride resting there in the back, I won't EVER go away from you! You've made me the happiest man on earth! Now more dancing!"

With that the band started on a fast jig and Elton leapt off the stage, grabbed Sarah and started whirling around the floor. I slipped off to the bar feeling much better about life and wondering if there was some hope for Sarah and me. As the night ended I sought out Sarah for one last dance and perhaps a tour of the castle. I found her in a small group and decided to push boldly in and ask for the dance. But when I reached the group, I heard Sarah elaborating on Raoul's family estate in Spain and how she loved to ride a young colt each morning and take in the beautiful land. I backed away and headed outside. So much for my newfound optimism.

It was a long trip back from Ireland. As the 747 screeched its tires on the hot Honolulu International Airport tarmac and settled in for the long taxi to the gate, I gazed out at the water. So what now? I was getting older, in my thirties already, and the woman of my dreams was not available—still. The hot air hit me as I headed down the jet way to the terminal. I shifted my carry-on to the other shoulder, entered the terminal and walked right into Laura's arms. That's right. Laura.

I know what you're thinking, Sandor. It's the same thing I was thinking.

What the hell is going on here? You're mooning over Sarah, but you've spent the last two years traipsing around Hawaii with Laura. You're passionate about someone you've never even kissed, but don't consider your relationship with Laura passionate, even though you sleep with her all the time. Are you deep into the 'grass is greener' syndrome? Is a 'bird in the hand' really worth two in the bush? What about four in the bush? Eight? Was Sarah really an 'eight bird girl?' How deep is the bush, and does it have thorns?

The more I thought about it, the more confused I got. I didn't know who to talk to, either. Elton was off on his honeymoon, MJ had stayed behind to tour Europe, and I couldn't very well call Sarah. The only person I was close to in Hawaii was Laura, another no-go. My parents and I had a good relationship, but I was not about to call them on this kind of issue. In fact, I had never told them anything of my feelings for Sarah, and they knew of Laura only as someone I occasionally dated. I had always been a private person, especially about relationships, and this confirmed it. I had no one to talk to.

That's when I turned to Talk Radio.

Say what you will about Talk Radio; at least it is always there. I started listening at work on those occasions—which were pretty much every day—when I stayed late to clean up my in-basket or wait for calls from our Pacific Rim partners as they arrived at work in the Far East time zone. It wasn't quite as personal as a friend, but for me that was a benefit. I could listen to a bunch of people with problems similar to mine talk to a psychologist, get some advice, whine about the advice, offer counter proposals, and finally accept, say thank you, and hang up. At no time did I actually have to bare my own soul, talk about my own shortcomings, or look a psychologist in the eye. And no group therapy. Geez, that would be the worst. Telling a bunch of strangers how screwed up you are and then listening to them tell you how to get right. I mean, my God, the only reason they are there is because they're screwed up. And they're going to help me?

"You know, Jack," Sandor interrupted my tirade, "there are benefits to group therapy. You should try it before you condemn it."

"No thanks, it's bad enough talking to a headless, faceless, bodiless person—or non-person—like you."

Sandor laughed again. "Go on with your story. Sorry for the interruption. What did you hear on talk radio?"

"Well, the advice I heard started to form a pattern. Things like, 'the attraction may fade, but the friendship lasts.' And 'love grows over time, and becomes stronger and deeper with the passing years.' If I thought of that in relation to me, it seemed as if Laura might be the one. We were good friends, and if my love grew over time, things would be great. Of course, Sarah and I were great friends, but I didn't think she was listening to Talk Radio so she could come to the conclusion that I was the one for her. I did hear a few folks say that they had persevered for many years and their one true love had finally realized that they were meant for each other. That gave me some hope for Sarah, but I knew I hadn't exactly persevered—heck, I hadn't even told her how I felt.

"I continued listening and contemplating my future for the next few months. I have always been patient, and if I thought more data would help a decision, I was willing to do the research. In this case, Talk Radio was not exactly pure research, but what the heck."

"Excuse me," Sandor interrupted, "but did you get a letter at this time?"

If I could have seen him, I would have stared at him blankly. "Could you be a little more specific?"

"A letter from MJ."

I hesitated as I thought. "Oh, you mean the one she wrote from England?"

"Yes, that one. Read it please."

Remembering how it worked with Steve's thesis and Sarah's letter, I concentrated on the letter. Once again, to my surprise, I saw it clearly.

Hi Gang!!!   *July 9th 1981*

I'm in heaven. Well, England actually. A little town on the coast called Chichester. But the heaven is not England or Chichester, it's The Body Shop. What a wonderful place to work!! Whoops, maybe I'm ahead of myself. You are all probably wondering why I am still on this side of the Atlantic. Let me back up a bit.

After Elton's wedding, that last night at Fitzpatrick's Castle, we all discussed our plans. Remember that I wanted to head off and explore Europe but couldn't figure out how to do that with my lack of cash. I decided to head down to England with one of Elton's cousins—you remember the one, tall with beautifully bright red hair—who was living outside of London a few hours. She let me stay with her while I wandered around England and tried to figure out how to see the rest of Europe. One day I was puttering around Chichester and happened upon a store called The Body Shop. It was very cool from the outside, with a dark green paint job on the bottom around wonderfully colorful window displays. The upper level was oddly shaped, rose to a point on one side, and was painted light blue with huge flowers and various colored bottles all around. I went in and had the best time. It smelled heavenly, and the women inside were so friendly, curious about the U.S., passionate about helping the world, and extremely knowledgeable about their products.

So what are their products, and what is their business? With your warped sense of humor Elton (which does kind of follow mine, I'll admit), I can guess what you are thinking. But no, The Body Shop is not a cheeky name for a funeral home. The Body Shop sells body cleansers and polishers, bath oils and salts, shampoos and conditioners, moisturizers and cosmetics. And instead of using all kinds of chemicals and man-made materials, they use natural products whenever possible. Things like cocoa butter, jojoba oil, almond oil, and aloe vera. The products are wonderful (Sarah, I'll send you some of their incredible bath products), I love to use them, and they are so easy to sell because my passion shows through. What a novel concept—to be passionate about your job. Oops, I'm getting ahead of myself again. Let's go back to that day I walked into the shop for the first time.

It was early evening, a few hours before closing. There were two women working in the store, both about my age. They began showing me products, a lotion to rub on here, a fragrance to smell there. As is my nature, I began asking questions, and they were delighted to help me. They had such unusual products that question after question popped off my tongue. How did a Honey and Oatmeal Scrub Mask work? What was Cucumber Cleansing Milk designed to cleanse? What was in Hawthorn Hand Cream? How—and why—did Seaweed and Birch Shampoo work? If I used Cocoa Butter Body Lotion would I taste like chocolate? And on and on. They answered all the questions in great detail, and seemed to love to talk about their products and their work.

They were spending so much time helping me that I began to feel guilty because I knew I didn't have much money to spend. They weren't neglecting their other customers, but when I arrived they had been stocking shelves, cleaning up and so forth and I knew from my waitress days that somebody still had to do those types of chores and it would probably be them after the store closed. So I told them that I was poor and I wouldn't feel bad at all if they went back to their tasks; I would be happy just looking at all the great stuff by myself.

"Well," one of the women said, "why don't you help us stock and we'll tell you all about what you're putting on the shelves. And you can tell us a little bit about America."

I thought that was a marvelous idea and told her so. She introduced herself as Aidre and together we stocked, cleaned and chatted about England, the U.S., Elton's wedding, and any number of other subjects that came up. I even helped a customer when the others were busy and the woman mistook me for sales staff. Since I had just asked the same questions about the product, I rattled off the answer like a pro. It was a kick, and the woman seemed pleased to know the information.

So pleased in fact, that she picked up several bottles of the product and bought them. After the woman left, Aidre gave out a low whistle.

"You're quite the sales woman aren't you?"

"Well, I've done my share of selling, and I've been a waitress also. That's a sales job mixed in with carrying heavy trays and trying not to trip and look a fool."

"You know," Aidre said, "Anita started out in the restaurant business also."

"Who's Anita?" I said.

"She started The Body Shop with her husband Gordon. Actually, in the beginning, a few years ago, they opened their first shop in Brighton, and he immediately went off to ride a horse from Buenos Aires to New York."

"He what?" I exclaimed.

"He went off to ride a horse from Buenos Aires to New York. It had been a dream of his since childhood."

"And left Anita to run the new shop by herself?"

"Right. That's when I came along to help."

"That is so cool," I said. "To actually fulfill your childhood dream, and to trust in your spouse so much that you just leave the new business to her."

"She is a remarkable woman," Aidre said.

"I would love to hear more about her and this shop," I said.

"Tell you what. Help me finish here and I'll treat you to a spot of dinner and a pint."

"You're on," I said, "and I'll come in tomorrow for however long you want to work off my debt."

"Nonsense on that. But come in whenever you like. I believe you are a kindred spirit, MJ."

And off we went to a pub and had wonderful fish and chips, a couple of pints and shared all kinds of stories. Aidre began to tell me after dinner that The Body Shop promotes social responsibility, working in the community, even doing whatever they could to help the world. One of Aidre's key workers was very concerned about the killing of whales and had requested six months off to help Greenpeace fight the whaling industry. The Body Shop wouldn't pay her to do this, but they did want to support her, so they had given their blessing and assured her she would have a job when she returned. But in the meantime Aidre needed someone to take her place for those six months. Someone who was passionate about the products and cared about the vision of business not just being a place to make money, but also a place to effect social change. And someone who would be willing to take a six-month assignment.

I thought about how great it would be to work at a place like that, and how I could save a few bucks to continue my travels around Europe. Before I knew what I was doing I had leaped out of my chair and was pointing emphatically at my chest.

"I'm the one you're looking for. It's me, Aidre!! I'm all those things you said and more. Please take me on. I'm perfect for this job."

She smiled at my enthusiasm and nodded.

"I thought it might be you when we started talking this afternoon. I had been wondering what I was going to do, and suddenly there you were. I don't believe in coincidences like that. There is some kind of plan going on, and you and I were meant to meet."

She stood up and opened her arms.

"Welcome to The Body Shop."

I jumped forward and hugged her, my first official act as a Body Shop employee.

I started the next day and it was totally grand!! Aidre and the other workers were so great, and the customers really love our shop. They love our enthusiasm, our style, our knowledge, and most of all the products. We get training in the products regularly, both from experienced staffers, and from Mark Constantine, who is the major supplier of The Body Shop products. He is an herbalist, which means he understands plants and natural substances, and how to put them together to make products like ours. He holds training sessions where he tells us what is in the products, where they come from, how they work, and even why they work. I just love the learning, and it makes us look so smart to our customers. Mark is a great guy, totally passionate about what he is doing, and his love and zeal for his work shows through. (Oh, and he is very cute, too!) We invariably leave the training sessions jazzed about our jobs and excited about the new products.

I also got to meet Anita. Her full name is Anita Roddick and, like I said, she and her husband Gordon run the company. She loves trading and sales and people and being out in public with staffers, customers, suppliers, whomever. He likes to stay behind the scenes, run the numbers, and hold down the fort so to speak. They make a great team. I envy their integration of life, work, love, and family. It is a wonderful model to aspire to.

Anyway, back to meeting Anita. I was stocking shelves late one day when this woman burst into the store. Her arms were full of posters and leaflets and her wild hair frizzed and bounced all about her head and shoulders. Her jeans were worn and faded and the frayed edges at the bottom brushed against her old sandals. Her long, baggy sweatshirt hung loosely from her shoulders and her eyes lit up the room. She came in at quite a pace and plopped her armload on the counter. I wasn't sure what to do. I thought she was working for some charity and wanted us to display her posters and I wasn't too sure of our policy on that. Lucky for me, Aidre jumped up and hugged her before I tried to run her out. She stayed for a few hours, and as we worked she told us great stories about her life on the road in search of new product ideas, dealing with new people and new ingredients, and also about how she views business in general. I felt like I had known her all my life. The stories were lively and funny, and even more compelling was how I felt about her views on business.

Certainly, I have never analyzed business like you, Jack, and never thought much about its role except when I needed money and was glad to get a job. Anita triggered something in me that I didn't know was there. I do want to earn a living, but I want to be passionate about it, be involved with it; I want to love what I'm doing and feel like I can make a difference in the world. She said people feel great and their spirits soar when they can satisfy their own material needs while at the same time serving the needs of others, honorably and humanely. After talking with Anita, I began thinking about why I am here on Earth in the first place. There must be a reason. I just can't buy that we are here for a few years and then we're dust. I feel like I do have a purpose. I just need to find it. I read a few lines in a little bookstore the next night that hit home. It said something like:

"Your life's work is to discover your life's work, then with all your heart to give yourself to it."

So that is my goal now, boys and girl. I am looking for my life's work. And I am going to live each day passionately, whatever I am doing. And I'll tell you—I am going to hang on here at *The Body Shop* for as long as I can. They may not be perfect, but they are trying damn hard to get there.

Cheerio,

MJ

P.S. Jack, would you mind xeroxing this letter and sending it to Sarah and Elton? I don't have their current addresses.

Thanks and love,

MJ

P.P.S. Saves postage too and you know I am broke...

I finished reading and paused as I thought about MJ's passion and the wealth of information in her letter. That was where Sandor wanted to go, too.

"What did you learn from her letter?" he asked.

"At the time, I would say nothing. I thought it was interesting and entertaining in an MJ kind of way, but I didn't pay much attention to it or its message."

"What about now?"

"Now I see I should have been paying attention, and if I had remembered Father Antonio's picnic saying—*There are no coincidences*—maybe I would have. Here I was desperately working to be promoted, to keep moving up, and MJ was showing me a model that inspirited a work force, made them want to come to work and made them passionate about their work. And I missed it. Not only that, she also touched on another important point—the integration of work and home life. I had no integration at that time, and I was contemplating long-term relationships—even marriage. What was I going to do if I did get married? How would I integrate the two? It would have been a smart move for me to consider these points before I made a decision."

"Did you?"

"No. I listened to Talk Radio for a few more months, and then the project was over. It had been very successful, and I was a golden boy at our corporate offices. As I packed up to leave Hawaii, my career was definitely on the rise. I had gambled with this assignment—and won. As for my love life...well, a draw at best. Sarah was off traveling, studying all kinds of healing, and building the life and career she wanted. Without me. Laura, on the other hand, was right there with me, and excited as heck about my successes at work.

"On the last night in Hawaii, she proposed to me. I didn't know what to say. I hadn't thought about this contingency. With my penchant for studying things, I probably would have been happy for years thinking, reading books, and listening to Talk Radio, and never making a decision. But Laura was persuasive. I think maybe she had been listening to Talk Radio, too. We were so close, she said. She understood my work ambitions—and supported them. We could talk about work since she was in the same environment. We had gotten closer and closer over the two years in Hawaii, and we would continue to grow. It was time to strengthen our commitment and become a true family. She ordered me another Mai Tai and continued the discussion. Three Mai Tais later, I said yes.

"Two weeks later we were married on the beach by a Justice of the Peace. Probably the first really rash thing I had ever done. I hesitated in calling my parents, MJ, Elton, and, of course, Sarah. I wasn't sure what they would think of my quick decision. And with Sarah, the last thing I wanted was for her to be staring at me as I said my vows. Luckily, she was in an ashram in India then, and I couldn't get through to her. I sent her a letter, with minimum postage. The proverbial slow boat method.

'The wedding was fine and my family and friends were supportive, of course. Sarah sent me congratulations a few weeks later."

"Of course, she would," Sandor mused. "She had to let you travel your own path."

"What's that supposed to mean?" I shot back a little too quickly.

"All in good time. Continue with your story."

chapter **nine**

"Well, that is the end of my wedding story. The story of how my first real relationship started. I kind of backed into it, if you know what I mean. Not something I am real proud of."

"Don't judge yourself," Sandor said. "Plenty of other people willing to do that." He paused as I reflected on his statement. But he wasn't looking for discussion. "Keep going with your story. What happened after the wedding?"

"Laura and I returned to the Santa Clara Valley as a couple and looked for a house. I now owned The Gatehouse—I had saved enough travel and bonus money the first year in Hawaii to buy it from Barbara, but Laura wanted us to start fresh with a house we both chose. That was understandable, but I insisted that we keep The Gatehouse as an investment and rent it out. We found a house and a year later we had a daughter— Elizabeth Ann. I adored her. But I didn't stop my brutal work schedule. This began to wear on Laura, who still 'understood' my work requirements, but felt that at least a small change was in order. She was right, of course, and I kept meaning to make some changes; but then the next big project came along, the next huge deadline, the next iron I had to pull out of the fire if I was to keep up my swift movement through the company. In 1985 I was promoted to General Manager. I was ecstatic. This put me into the executive ranks with parking passes and executive dining rooms. And much more access to the people at the top of the company. I was really on my way.

"But things at home were becoming more of a struggle. Laura was unhappy and pushing for change. I wrestled with the time commitments and the integration of the two demands. It would have been a good time to strengthen my relationship with Laura and spend more time with Elizabeth. But I had a large organization, almost 400 people, and I wasn't at all sure how to manage that size group. I struggled in this setting for the better part of a year, trying to be the leader I needed to be and feeling increasingly uneasy about how much time I was spending to do that."

"And did you receive some help with being a great leader and some advice on your family?" Sandor asked.

"Yes," I said my heart sinking as I remembered another "coincidence" that I had missed. "Vincent."

"Tell me about Vincent."

"OK," I said with a sigh wondering if everyone's life was like this in review. Signs, guideposts and "coincidences" and us too busy to notice.

Vincent was a colleague of mine, perhaps twenty years older and very successful in our company. He was one of our executive VPs, and conventional wisdom said he was one of two or three who might be our next CEO. I liked Vincent. He was a quiet man overall, but exuded a strength I could feel. I felt like I learned more from him—just from watching him—than from any of the other executives. As I participated in my first executive council meetings I observed the interaction. It seemed as if everyone was competing for the favor and attention of the CEO. Comments were frequently made that were very obvious to all, or perhaps on the periphery of the discussion, but allowed the person to exhibit some knowledge or opinion, to shine a little bit, so to speak. I quickly recognized several things.

First, just as in most meetings of my career, a good part of these meetings was posturing. The comments and discussions weren't really intended to further the aims of the organization, team, or company, but rather to build the ego and career of the one saying it.

Second, I recognized I was guilty of doing it also.

And third, time after time I saw that Vincent did not play that game. His comments were thoughtful and measured and always insightful. He listened intently, observed carefully, and said the truth as he saw it, regardless of whose side of the argument that put him on. I was never close to men and women with whom I worked, mostly because of my competitive nature. And saying I was close to Vincent is an overstatement, but I did admire him and welcomed any chance to talk with him. I felt no competition with Vincent. I'm sure that was partly due to his obvious seniority to me, but it was also because I felt no competition coming from him. He seemed to have no ego at all, giving credit, accepting blame, and presenting ideas, all with the same grace and dignity.

Now, I don't want to make it sound as if I thought Vincent was a hero and I idolized him. That's way too strong. I mean, maybe Vincent is a modern day hero, but at the time I would never have known, nor would I have talked about him like this. It was more of a feeling then. I felt good around him, peaceful, and I always looked forward to assignments with him. As I think back I am remembering why. He was an extraordinary man.

So when he called one day and asked me to lunch—his treat—I immediately said yes. Not only for all the reasons I cited above, but because a few weeks earlier a new CEO had been named at our company. And it wasn't Vincent. He had clearly been one of the top candidates, and I was wondering what had happened. Why hadn't he been selected? How was he feeling? I figured he must be devastated. At his age, this was likely his last chance at the top spot. After all those years of work he had failed. My stomach hurt just thinking about that possibility.

Vincent took me to a small place that served Mediterranean food. It was my first time in a Mediterranean restaurant and I wasn't even sure what Mediterranean food was. Vincent, however, had obviously been there before, because the owner rushed out to meet him and they embraced in a "hug-greeting" that until then I had only seen in old European movies.

We sat down and after ordering an appetizer of flat bread with a chunky, paste-like substance called hummus to spread on it (it was actually pretty good), Vincent started to talk.

"Jack, it was good of you to come."

"Wouldn't have missed it, Vincent," I replied.

"Do you have any idea why I invited you here today?" he asked.

"Well," I said stalling for time. "I suppose perhaps it's because…" I paused still searching for a plausible reason.

Finally I decided to just tell the truth.

"I guess I thought you might want to talk about your getting passed over for CEO. I'm sure I'm probably not your best friend or anything, but you know I like you and think highly of you, and I thought maybe you'd want to vent a bit."

"Oh, that," he said waving his hand. "No, that's not important." He looked at me with a sly grin. "But if you want me to tell you about it after we're done with our real discussion, I will."

I nodded quickly. He already knew I was desperate to hear about how the corporate politics had played out.

"No, the reason I wanted to talk with you today has to do with you," he said.

"Me?" I said weakly. This caught me by surprise.

"I'm worried about you, Jack." He paused from his task of spreading hummus on his flatbread to look at me gently.

"About me?" I had no idea where he was going. In my entire work life no one had ever talked about **me**. My work, my position, my vision for the organization, but not about me. And I could see he was truly concerned. I felt a rush of warmth that he cared about me, and also a surge of fear that he might be heading into the uncharted waters of my emotions and feelings.

"Yes, about you," he said. "You're smart, successful, moving up rapidly. You could be CEO someday."

I tried to suppress an involuntary smile at that last remark as Vincent continued.

"But you're not on a path of fulfillment, enlightenment, and true happiness."

I stared at him blankly trying to find the words to protest. They were nowhere to be found.

"You're on a path questing for something that's not real. And that will lead to disappointment, disillusionment, frustration, and probably an early death."

I was stunned. People at work just didn't talk like this. Occasionally we'd had those conversations at The Gatehouse; and in the deep reaches of my mind I remembered my parents offering their words of wisdom about life that I had largely ignored—except for the one speech that said work hard and achieve. But nothing at work. Vincent was touching on things that were so far from my conscious thought patterns each day that I couldn't even find questions to try to understand. Finally I grasped onto one piece.

"I'm on a path questing for something that's not real? What does that mean? What's not real?"

"Achievement isn't real. Titles, power, awards, plaques, magazine covers aren't real. They feel good in the short term, but what do they mean?" He gazed at me levelly.

"When did you have your last promotion?" he asked.

"About a year ago. From Director to General Manager."

"And how often in the last six months have you even thought about that?"

"Pretty much never."

"What are you thinking about?" He looked at me hard. "Honestly."

"Well, honestly, getting promoted to vice-president."

"Of course. Thank you for being honest. And when you make VP it will be Senior VP you'll be thinking about, then Executive VP, then CEO and Chairman of the Board."

I grinned. "That sounds like a pretty good progression."

He relaxed a bit and smiled. "Yes, that does sound good now. But let me ask you this. What will it take to get there? Long hours, total devotion, live, eat, breathe your goal?"

I nodded slowly.

"And then when you're CEO, you'll do great things."

I nodded vigorously, beaming this time.

"For whom?" He looked at me expectantly.

I was blank. I was sure there was a trick here. What was he looking for me to say? He continued to wait patiently.

I took a deep breath and thought about our mission and goals statement. There it was. Our recently revised statement had said that our goal was to raise shareholder value. That would take care of the owners of the company and ensure we could raise money easily though stock offerings. Since some of our employees held stock, it would help them also. That was it.

"For the shareholders," I told him, perhaps a bit smugly. "I would do great things for the shareholders."

"Why do you care about them?" he asked.

I recited the above reasons.

"You really buy that?"

I was stopped cold again.

"Well, yes," I stuttered. Vincent was an Executive VP. How could he be questioning our key mission and goals statement? "Don't you?"

"No, of course not. How long has it been since we raised money in a stock offering?"

"I don't know," I admitted.

"Twenty years."

"Twenty years?"

"That's right. And how many of our employees own our stock?"

"I don't know that either."

"About 25%. But of that number, less than 5% own an amount that might be termed significant. And they are almost all executives."

"Oh," I muttered.

"Now tell me this. Do you really think the true owners of this company are the shareholders?"

I thought a bit.

"Technically, yes. Aren't they?"

"Technically yes, they are," Vincent said. "But, in reality, how do a bunch of institutions and a few small investors own a company? Do they care, really care, about the company?"

"They care if it's profitable," I said.

"Exactly. But what is the company made of? Profits?"

"No," I admitted, "that's an outgrowth of other aspects of the company."

"What other aspects?" he pressed.

"Plants, parts, plans, marketing, sales, strategies, resources...."

"What resources?" he interjected.

"Money, equipment, facilities, people..."

"People," he almost shouted. "People are the heart of the company. Do the shareholders know any of the people?"

"No, of course not. Except for the few shareholders who work in the company."

"Do the shareholders care about the people?" he continued.

I paused then answered. "I'd say no, except insofar as they make the share price rise."

"What happens to the stock price when we lay off a bunch of people?"

"Well, my experience here, and my recollection from my MBA program, is that share price often rises."

"That's true," he confirmed. "And why does it rise?"

"Because the company is cutting costs and that usually makes the company more profitable," I recited from memory.

"Is that good for the shareholders?"

"Sure, price goes up, they make money."

"Is it good for the people of the company?"

"Not for the ones laid off," I said glibly.

"And not for the others either," he said sternly. "They are under great stress. Watching their friends go out the door. Picking up extra workloads. And worrying that maybe they're next."

"You're not saying that all lay-offs are bad, are you?"

"No, I'm not saying that. Sometimes, to get through tough times, tough steps are needed. And I'm also not saying that stock price is unimportant. There are benefits to a strong stock. But what I am trying to get across to you is that shareholders don't care about the people, and the people *are* the company. So when you say you're going to do great things as CEO, the 'For whom' had better be for them. Your partners in the company. Your fellow souls here and now."

His passion was at a peak and I remember thinking that he loved these folks. All 30,000 of them. I wasn't sure what to make of it. He snapped me out of my thought. He was smiling easily again. Then he said,

"Perhaps we're a bit off the subject, Jack. I came here because I was worried about you. Here are a few pieces of advice. I hope you take them to heart. First, slow down. Breathe a little. It is okay to stop and smell those roses.

"Second, take care of life—the whole of life. Especially your family. Careers will work themselves out.

"Third, don't live to fulfill other people's expectations. Do what's right for you. Not them.

"And, finally, take care of your own spirit. Make sure you take time to do those things that uplift you, and charge the battery of your spirit."

He paused, stood, and looked down at me. "I have to go. Let this sink in a bit. I'd be happy to talk later."

He headed for the door, stopping halfway to hug the owner and pass him some money.

"Wait," I called. "How do I take care of my own spirit? What things uplift spirit?" I was struggling. "What do *you* do to uplift your spirit?"

He smiled, "I paint, talk to good friends, play with my grand-kids, meditate, write poetry, ride my Harley, play squash, and the best—I try to help others. So thanks for coming today, Jack. You've helped uplift my spirit."

Then he turned and disappeared though the door. I was so stunned I forgot to ask what had happened with the CEO job.

I sat in the silence of my finished story. I needed a little time to think before I started talking to Sandor again. So many themes running through my head. Like the idea of teachers coming to help. It didn't seem as if I had been ready in my life for teachers, but it was clear they had come. And at very good times. Especially Vincent. He was just what I had needed. I had been going as fast as I could towards my goal. I never stopped to smell the roses. Hell, I didn't even water them. I didn't do things to uplift my spirit; I didn't even know what those things were any more. I consistently chose work over family, friends, anything really. And in the back of my mind I often wondered why I was so obsessed with being CEO. Was it for me, or was I responding to old messages of achievement from my childhood, or fighting to show I was good enough—even though I was Asian—to lead a major company?

I also needed to hear about the people of the company. Vincent's questions made it clear to me that I viewed them as just another resource, not the heart of the company. So Vincent and his message had really been a Godsend to me, delivered just in time.

Of course, I ignored it.

Not intentionally. I was struck by the conversation and impressed by Vincent and his outlook on life. But have you ever heard or seen something that you knew was right for you and then not done it? You didn't intend to not do it, but life just got in the way. You had a family crisis, a big deliverable at work, a hectic travel schedule, a new job, money problems, or whatever. You were distracted from the message and soon it faded.

It was clear now that I had missed a critical message. It had touched on all aspects of my fouled up life. Feeding the spirit, paying attention to my family, reducing stress and watching my physical health, focusing on the people at work—not only so their lives would be better, but also so that their ideas could come out, so their hearts and minds and creativity could be engaged, so the productivity and profitability of the company would soar.

Letting that message from Vincent fade proved very costly. The first price I had to pay was family. Eighteen months after my talk with him, Laura left me. And, of course, took Elizabeth with her. Watching Laura walk out the door hurt; but seeing Elizabeth in her arms—just three and not understanding what was happening— broke my heart. But I knew I deserved it. Looking back, I was lucky Laura stayed as long as she did.

I tried to talk her into coming back and giving me another try. But Laura was what I call a "threshold" person. She had great tolerance and could put up with a lot. But once she passed her threshold, she was done. She had had enough of me and my ways and wanted a different life for her and Elizabeth.

And, as she put it, "frankly, Jack, I don't think you'll ever change."

"Jack," Sandor broke in, "you have been quiet for some time. What are you thinking about?"

I sighed. "Just how dense I can be, and the cost of my denseness."

"Vincent's message was a good one, wasn't it?"

"Yes, and looking back I can't believe I missed it."

"I bet Laura wishes you had been more perceptive."

"Ouch, that stings."

"I wasn't trying to hurt you. It just seems an obvious point."

"Well, obvious or not, it's accurate. That's what I meant by the cost of my denseness. She left me and moved in with her parents. We sold the house and there I was, home alone. The only good part was the 'home' was The Gatehouse. I threw the renters out and moved back in."

"So, there you were, depressed, alone, kind of at rock bottom. What did you do then?"

"The only thing I knew how to do well. Worked harder and longer and tried to keep from thinking about my failures. My diet went to hell, exercise was forgotten, I tipped a few too many bottles...and I was promoted again. Funny how much you can accomplish if you work 80 to 100 hours a week. I wasn't happy, but I was on my way to my goal of being CEO. And that was the only thing I seemed to be good at. I pressed the pedal to the metal and shot towards the finish line. What I really needed was another intervention—someone like Vincent to prod me again and get me thinking about the really important things in life. But he had taken an early retirement to join an expedition that was trying to sail a Kon-Tiki type of raft from Polynesia to Easter Island."

I sighed again. "Seeing Elizabeth on the weekends I was in town was my only joy. Other than that, I was alone. At home and at work. Just alone."

chapter **ten**

"Jack...Jack. Jack, listen to me. You seem lost again. Wake up. It's time to continue with your story."

"What?" I managed to get out.

"It's time to move on," I heard Sandor say. "I know this can be hard, but we must finish."

"It *is* hard reliving your life's screw-ups. And why *must* we finish? I don't suppose you'll tell me that, will you?"

"All in good time. First, the story."

"Okay," I grumbled. I didn't have the energy to put up a fight. "Give me a minute here." I tried to relax and put myself back in time again.

"The next few years passed quickly after Laura left me, bigger jobs and promotions my reward for the punishing work schedule I followed. I didn't mind, though. The more I worked and focused on the company, the less time I had to think about all my screw-ups in life and relationships." I paused as I recalled some of my earlier learnings. "I guess without ever really thinking about it, I was just distracting myself from the real purpose of my life. Not that I knew what that purpose was, but working eighty hours a week is a good way to make sure you never figure it out."

"Yes," Sandor said softly, "it certainly is." Now it was his turn to pause. I wasn't sure if he was trying to make sure the lesson sunk in, but finally he continued. "What about the invitation?"

"Not twenty questions again," I said impatiently. "Which invitation?"

"The one from Sarah," he replied.

"Oh, that one," I said lamely. I had to give him credit. He did know how to ask the hard question. "Yeah, I remember that one."

"Tell me what you felt when you got the letter out of the mailbox," Sandor said.

I thought back. "I remember it was a Saturday and I had been at work all day. I stopped by the mailbox when I got home, and my heart jumped as I saw the letter from Sarah.

"I didn't know why it jumped. I wasn't expecting anything from her, and I certainly had no cause to believe that a letter from her would contain anything but friendship material. But it did jump, and when I took a minute and tried to really be honest with myself, I did know why. I had never gotten over her. She was still the one etched deep in my heart, my first true love." I laughed. "Sounds silly saying it now like it was some big revelation. But I tried very hard not to think about her each day, and when I did think of her, to view her as a good friend, like Elton or MJ. But seeing a letter from her had triggered something inside me; maybe, just maybe, some inner voice was shouting, this letter is significant."

"So you were excited when you opened the letter?" Sandor asked.

I shook my head. "No. I immediately squashed all my hopes and opened the letter in a businesslike fashion. I have never been comfortable when my emotions are out of control, especially when it comes to Sarah. What was that Jack Nicholson line? *'You want the truth? You can't handle the truth!'*

"That's me for sure. I knew I couldn't handle the truth about Sarah, so I had always built stories in my mind. Sometimes we were just friends and I would think how lucky I was to have a friend like her; other times I would think that she secretly liked me too, but I was too busy now to build the relationship. Always pretending. This time, as I slit the envelope I told myself how nice it was to get a friendly letter from Sarah updating her life. No expectations."

"What did you find?"

"An invitation."

"How did you feel then?"

"I lost it. The whole facade cracked. I remember my face flushed so fast it felt like it had ignited. I couldn't breathe. I just prayed. 'Not a wedding invitation, please God, not a wedding.'"

"Did you think she might get married?"

"I had no reason to. MJ had told me a year earlier that Raoul had returned to Spain to practice in his hometown. But had he come back to the U.S.? Was Sarah going to Spain? Or had she found someone new? I tore it open as I continued my rapid-fire, Hail-Mary-like prayers—'no wedding, no wedding, please God, no wedding.'"

"Were your prayers answered?"

"Yes. It wasn't a wedding invitation."

"What was it?"

"An invitation to the grand opening celebration of her new wellness center on June 3rd, 1989. There was a map attached, and a note from Sarah. The center was called The East/West Holistic Wellness Center, and it was in a place called the 'Roosevelt District' in Seattle, Washington."

"Do you remember what the note from Sarah said?"

"Yes" I said confidently. "This one I definitely remember."

Hi Jack!

I do hope you will be able to come up for the grand opening. I know how busy you VPs are, but it would really mean a lot to me if you could make it. We have been through quite a bit together—you, me, Elton and MJ—and I want to share this moment with all of you. And you, Jack, with your support of me after I quit my residency, were more instrumental than you know in me finding my true path.

I truly hope you can find a way to spend a few days up here in the great northwest.

Love,

Sarah

P.S. Don't bother with a hotel, you can stay with me.

"What did you feel when you read that note for the first time?" Sandor asked.

"I was shaking. For such a short letter, it had been like a roller coaster ride. First, she said it would mean a lot if I made it—that was exciting. Then, she lumps me in with MJ and Elton—just one of the gang—nothing exciting about that. Then I get credit for helping her in her time of need—that felt good, but only for a moment, because I knew I offered the help to support my own agenda—nothing saintly there. Finally, another plea for me to come and the great 'P.S.'

"By the end of it I wasn't sure what to think—or feel, for that matter. One thing I did know. I was going to Seattle. I called my secretary and left a message for her to block out a long weekend on my calendar."

"What made you so adamant about going?" Sandor asked. "I'm sure you could have found some acceptable excuse."

I nodded. "Yeah, I could have. But I knew I needed to go. And not only because I wanted to see Sarah. Not only because I harbored hopes about a future relationship. I needed to ask her about something. How was I instrumental in helping her find her 'true path?' And did she have any ideas how I could find mine?"

"Sounds like something was starting to stir in that body of yours, Jack." Sandor spoke with what I thought—or imagined—was a hint of approval. "So tell me the story of Seattle now. What happened in the emerald city?"

It didn't start very smoothly. The grand opening was set for Saturday, the 3rd. I knew MJ and Elton were coming in on Friday, so I decided to arrive on Thursday. I wanted some time alone with Sarah. The day came for my departure, and a crisis erupted at work. Wasn't this always the way, I thought, as I headed for the boardroom and the emergency meeting. I hardly ever plan anything personal and the one time I do, all hell breaks loose. I asked my secretary to cancel my plane reservation for that afternoon and stand by. The grand opening wasn't until the day after tomorrow, and I was going to make it one way or the other.

The crisis turned out to be a "show cause" notice from the Air Force on one of our contracts. This type of notice was sent out when the government customer believed you were in big trouble on your contract and wouldn't meet your schedule or cost commitments. It was a very big deal— your last chance to fix things before the contract was canceled. You literally had to "show cause" as to why they should not terminate your contract, and also show how you were going to recover from your present troubles.

This was not good news for Dynamics, but the good news for me was that it wasn't one of my contracts that received the notice. That gave me hope that I could still slip away to Seattle. But first we had to decide as a leadership team how to handle the problem and what resources to commit to it. We spent Thursday and Friday planning and mobilizing our forces. Part of the problem was that one of our sub-contractors was not performing well, and this was an area where I knew I could help. I was considered the company expert in dealing with "subs" and promised the program manager and his VP that I would have recommendations in ten days for dealing with the problem. Then I assembled three of my best people and told them to get on site and gather all the data they could about the sub-contractor, the performance problems, and the Air Force perception of the problems in relation to the sub. Have it all ready, I told them, to brief me at 7:00 a.m. sharp next Wednesday. Then I caught the 6:30 p.m. flight Friday evening to Seattle. My return was for Sunday afternoon—about six hours after MJ and Elton left. I was determined to get some alone time with Sarah.

I arrived in Seattle about 8:30 p.m. I signed for my rental car and threw my bag in the trunk. Sarah had offered to pick me up, but I wanted lots of flexibility. Not only to sightsee and tool around with MJ and Elton, but to flee if I wasn't strong enough to handle whatever the week might bring with Sarah. I scanned the map and then headed north towards Sarah's home in Seattle's "Queen Anne" neighborhood. I ended up on something Sarah called the Alaskan Way Viaduct that passed right by the Kingdome where the Mariners played baseball and the Seahawks football. I had seen the inside on TV a few times and that looked okay, but the outside was a different story. A monstrous, dirty, grayish concrete structure; it was an eyesore.

But just past that was one of the most beautiful sights I had ever seen from a highway, rivaling the many incredible views from the Bay Area bridges and Highway 280. As I looked to my left, Puget Sound opened up, ferryboats cutting across the waters, islands and peninsulas jutting out, the Olympic Mountains, crystal clear in the distance, snow still capping the tops. The sun was trying to hide behind the mountains and the reds, yellows and golds raced across the sky in all directions. I slowed and took it all in.

My heart swelled with pleasure and anticipation. Definitely a good way to start the trip. Suddenly invigorated and optimistic, I gunned the car towards Sarah's.

The house reminded me of The Gatehouse. An old Victorian, it exuded character and charm. It turned out that Queen Anne was on top of a hill, and from the road it looked like the second story of the house might have a similar view to the one I had just seen of the Olympics and Puget Sound. I didn't know if Sarah was renting or actually owned it, but it was clear that she had once again found that "special place" to live. I grabbed my bag and headed up the walk.

Inside, the reunion was going full swing. Elton was making Irish coffees in the kitchen, while MJ and Sarah were choosing tapes and CDs from the seventies—Elton John's Yellow Brick Road was currently playing. I hugged each of them. Elton danced me around.

"Don't you love this *Elton* guy?" he asked.

I nodded. I loved both Elton guys.

I looked at the three of them. Maire had been unable to get away from work and Sarah's parents were flying in tomorrow morning so for tonight it was just the four of us. It was wonderful to be together again; it truly made me feel great. Just being around them gave me a happiness and joy that, as I reflected on it, had been sadly lacking in my life. The only comparable times were when I was with Elizabeth.

We didn't stay up long that night, with the grand opening set for tomorrow. As we cleaned up and prepared to head for bed, I asked Sarah if I could check the baseball scores on the TV. The San Francisco Giants were in a pennant race, albeit an early one since it was only June.

"Sure, Jack," she said as she scooped up some coffee cups and headed for the kitchen. "But I don't have cable, so you'll only be able to get the local channels."

"No problem," I said although I had secretly hoped I could find ESPN. "The local news will at least have the scores."

I found a news station and they promised sports right after the commercial break. The first commercial started playing and Sarah suddenly started shouting, stopping everyone in their tracks.

"Hey hold on everyone, watch this commercial."

The commercial showed a man walking into the kitchen as the table is being set for dinner. Two women are there, one 25 or 30 years older than the other. The younger woman has an apron on, this appears to be her kitchen. The man sniffs the air and with a smile says: "What's for dinner." The younger woman, obviously his wife, answers that she has made his favorite dish, a spicy Italian one. Quickly the older woman speaks up, and we find out it is the man's mother.

"Ted has never been able to eat that. It gives him heartburn."

Ted quickly jumps in.

"Not if I take these first," and he proudly flashes a packet of one of the leading heartburn and antacid pills. "If I take one thirty minutes prior to eating, I don't feel a thing."

Sarah jumped up, turned down the TV, and faced us.

"This is one of the big areas we are focusing on at the center. Educating people to listen to their bodies. The first time I saw that commercial was a few months ago, and I lost it. 'Ted,' I shouted at the TV, 'did you every consider why your body is rebelling against that stuff?'

"Of course, Ted isn't listening, so he covers up the symptoms and goes on. When he gets a headache, he pops several aspirin and goes on. When he's tired in the morning, he drinks two cups of coffee; when he's agitated in the evening, he has a few drinks; when he can't sleep, he takes a pill and on and on he goes." Sarah was getting passionate. I loved to see her that way, not only because I loved to see her passionate, but also because she often had passion about subjects that were important to mankind in general, not just to her. I admired that.

She went on.

"His body—and mind for that matter—is giving him one clear signal after another that something is wrong. But Ted has been conditioned that in our society you don't listen to your body and try to understand and treat the cause. Instead, you attempt to mask the symptoms and go on living the life that's causing the problem.

"After I saw this commercial, I began to wonder how my team at the East/West Holistic Wellness Center would react to a problem like Ted's. Tomorrow, I'll show you how we handled a case like that."

"Sounds great," MJ said.

"Yes, it does," Elton seconded.

I didn't say anything. I took those "masking" pills several times a week. Sarah took MJ and Elton up to their rooms while I watched the sports. Then Sarah showed me to my room. It was simple, but special—it exuded warmth, love, caring, and peace. A great place to not only sleep, but to rest a tired soul.

"I am so glad you could make it, Jack," Sarah said as she lit three candles on the dresser. "I know how demanding your job is, and I was hoping you could work things out."

"I'm glad I made it, too. I really wanted to come, but now that I am here, I can see I really *needed* to come. You three are so special to me, and the feelings I get around you all are so powerful. Thanks for inviting me." I paused then pushed on. "And I do want to talk to you about some things."

"Really? Like what?"

"I'll tell you later. You have more important things to think about now—like a grand opening."

She smiled brightly. "Yes, and I can't wait for all of you to see it. I'm so excited."

And you could certainly see that. Her cheeks were flushed and her eyes sparkled.

"Sarah, how about if we talk Sunday after MJ and Elton leave?"

"Outstanding! That will be great, Jack." She nodded towards the bed. "Sleep well and don't forget to blow out the candles before you fall asleep."

I nodded. She smiled, leaned forward and kissed me on the cheek, and backed out of the room.

My own smile appeared. So far, so good.

The next morning, Sarah was up early and off to the clinic to get ready for the big day. She had planned displays, demonstrations, lectures, free check-ups, drawings, health quizzes, prizes, and refreshments, topped off by a special "invitation only" dinner at the Center. MJ, Elton, and I had our own plans for the morning. Coffee and fresh scones at a local bakery Sarah had recommended, then a trip out to Pike Place Market, a local icon situated right by the water. We planned to arrive at the clinic in the afternoon, see all there was to see, then stay for the special dinner and celebration.

After the scones—which were hot and so good I ate two—we got to Pike Place just in time to see big fish flying across the Market. As we got closer we realized it was the famous fish market workers who fired the fresh fish at each other at high speeds, with lots of shouting and bantering. Workers who sold the fish out in front would holler instructions back to the ones behind the counter, then whip the fish at them. The "catchers" would hold up some butcher paper and haul the fish in, filet it if required, wrap it and charge the customer. With several selling and catching, and all of them hawking, hollering and cajoling, it made for quite a scene.

We toured the market, had a light lunch on a balcony overlooking the action, and caught up on each other's lives. It felt good to be away from the rush of the office and with people I cared about. After a short walk to settle the lunch, we headed to the Center. We parked across the street and looked over. The sign out front made it clear we were at the right place.

East/West Holistic Wellness Center

It was a hand-painted wood sign rich in blues and greens, and featuring a mural with mountains and water prominent. Below it a temporary sign hailing the grand opening waved gently in the breeze. The building itself had clearly been a house in its previous life, but it seemed large enough for a business from the outside. The paint was fresh, the small yard groomed, the front door open. Very inviting, I thought.

The three of us crossed the street and headed up the stairs to the front door. We were warmly greeted by a young woman who obviously had been waiting for us.

"Well, you must be MJ, Elton, and Jack. Welcome to the Center! I'm Nancy, our office administrator. Sarah has told me lots about the three of you."

"And all the good stuff is true," Elton quipped, "but don't believe that other stuff about Jack. I can vouch for him. He is not as weird as he looks."

I boxed him on the arm and threatened to give him a "stooge" poke in the eye. He responded with a high-pitched "whup, whup, whup, oh, a wise guy, eh?" and drew his hand up to the bridge of his nose in defense.

Nancy was staring and did not appear to be a Stooge fan.

"Let me show you to the back room. Sarah is giving a demonstration there." She turned to lead us down the hall and as she did MJ whacked both of us and whispered fiercely. "Will you guys try not to act like school kids? For heaven's sake, this is Sarah's Center and these folks work for her. Do you want them to think her best friends act like they're ten years old?"

"No," Elton agreed solemnly, then his face took on the look of a leprechaun. "I was thinking eight years old would be better." We both tried to stifle our laughter as we ducked under MJ's next barrage. Nancy tried to ignore us and quietly pushed open a door and motioned us in. On the side of the door the room was labeled *The Gathering Place.* We slipped in quietly so we wouldn't disturb Sarah, who appeared to be in mid-demonstration, just calling for volunteers from the audience. A young man answered the call and began to make his way to the front of the room. As he did I took the opportunity to look around. The room was about 25 feet by 30 feet and had several desks around the outskirts and some easels with flip chart paper hanging on them in the corners. The walls were textured in some way, or at least the paint looked different. MJ saw me staring at the wall and whispered,

"They're color washed."

"Oh," I said and nodded, but it really didn't help much; I didn't know what "color washed" meant.

The young man had reached the front and I turned my attention towards him and Sarah.

"So we've talked about the importance of nutrition and diet to our health. And how putting the proper fuel in the body is a big step towards better health and *preventing* sickness. Let's see if we can demonstrate that." She turned to the young man, who appeared to be in his mid-twenties. "Thanks for volunteering. What's your name?"

"Nic," he said, "with a 'c' and no 'k.'"

"That's an unusual spelling, Nic, but I like it. I have a Greek South African friend who spells his name like that. Okay, put your arm out to the right for me please. Like this, straight out from the side and parallel to the ground." She demonstrated by holding her arm straight out from her side so it formed a continuous line from the neck through the shoulder and out to the fingertips.

"Good, Nic. Now, I am going to grab your wrist with one hand and pull down. Do you think I can pull your arm down to your side so your hand touches your hip?"

Nic was a little embarrassed. He was about six feet tall and weighed at least 195 or so. There didn't appear to be much fat on him and his muscles were well defined. It was clear that as he looked at Sarah and her slender frame—which held maybe 110 pounds—that he didn't think she had any chance of moving his arm. He hesitated, not wanting to offend her.

"Come on, Nic, you don't have to worry about hurting my feelings. Do you think I can put that hand against your hip or not?"

He smiled. "I don't think so, Doctor."

"Well, let's try."

Sarah stood next to Nic's arm and with her left hand grasped his wrist and pulled down. The arm moved maybe an inch before Nic stiffened and held firm. After about five seconds of pulling down Sarah stopped, wiped her brow, and looked out at the audience, which numbered about 25.

"How many of you thought I could do it?" Only one small girl raised her hand. Sarah turned to her. "Bless you, sweetheart, for your faith." She turned back to the crowd. "Now if I give Nic a small package to hold with his other hand, how many of you think I could pull his arm down then?"

"How heavy is the package?" someone called out.

"Very light," she replied. She looked around. "No takers. Okay, let's try it again then." She handed Nic a package that looked like a regular plastic bag with carrots inside. "Hold it against your left side with your left hand. Now, here we go." She pulled again with no better results than the first time.

"All right, one more time. If I switch that package for this one," she held up the same size package with a white crystal inside like sugar or salt, "does anyone think I can do it then?" She paused strategically. "Anyone want to bet?"

The audience hesitated, a bit shocked at the challenge. That gave Sarah her opening.

"What about you, sir," she called out and pointed to the back of the room. "Yes, you," she pointed again and I realized with a start that she was pointing at me.

"Well…" I started hesitantly, but she cut me off.

"How about this. You and I will each put up ten dollars and the winner can take the twenty dollars and donate it to their favorite charity. What do you say?"

She was grinning mischievously, and I had to admit that I wanted to see what the heck she had up her sleeve. I walked towards the front of the room.

"You're on," I said and held my ten dollars aloft.

"Very good," she said. She turned back to Nic and gave him the bag and helped him position it against his side.

"Ready, one, two, three, and…" with that she pulled. His arm came down and slapped against his side. The audience gasped and I was staring with my mouth open when Sarah lifted the ten dollars from my fingers.

"Thanks for playing," she said under her breath. She turned back to Nic. He was in absolute shock and was trying to talk.

"I don't think I was ready, Doctor. Can I try it again?"

"Sure," she said and did it again. He was shaking his head and looking at her like she was a magician. She thanked him and he headed back to his seat.

"Thank you, sir," she said bowing slightly to me. "The Children's Home of Washington will appreciate your donation."

I smiled and bowed back and moved against the side wall as she continued.

"I apologize for my parlor trick, ladies and gentlemen," she said smiling. "There really is no secret to it. Any of you can do it. Indeed, Nic *was* weaker when he held this sugar against himself. It disrupted his energy field, so to speak, in a way that carrots did not. Now imagine if we put a lot of sugar, or other less desirable substances, *in* our bodies. When I speak of our clinic here and our commitment to look at every aspect of your body, mind and spirit so we can not only heal your illnesses, but also *prevent* them, I am very serious. And what goes in your body, and your energy— or chi as it is called in the East—as well as many other factors must all be considered.

"When I left my MD residency eight years ago, it was because I felt that many of those other factors, as well as many possible cures, were ignored because they weren't understood here in the west. And it didn't seem like many of the doctors and hospital administrators wanted to understand. There wasn't openness in allopathic medicine towards alternative treatments. So I studied healing practices around the world, became a doctor of Naturopathic medicine here in Seattle at Bastyr University, then went to the Mayo Clinic to finish my MD work. The Mayo Clinic really started integrated medicine almost a hundred years ago and their coordinated, collaborative, and caring approach to patients taught me so much. When I decided to open my own practice, I knew I needed to be in an open, supportive environment where all possibilities—including traditional Western medicine, which is also known as allopathic medicine—could be seen as legitimate alternatives. That is why I opened this Center. I hope you will give us a chance to serve you.

"Thank you, and don't forget the juices, spritzers, and snacks in the front."

The audience clapped and after some questions they made their way out. A few lingered to get in a private question, including Nic, whose face still registered his disbelief. Soon though, Elton, MJ and I were the only ones left, and we each hugged and congratulated Sarah. Elton had loved the demonstration—especially the part where I lost ten bucks—and wanted to hear more about that.

"I'll explain more tonight, Elton," Sarah said. "But now let me show you around a bit before the next demonstration." She pointed up to the top of the wall, which was cantilevered and had some writing on it.

"This is our vision statement, and you'll find it in a few more places in the Center as well as on our business card. It says what we are all about."

Treat the whole body, mind and spirit of our patients to promote wellness and prevent and/or heal illness and injury.

"Obviously," Sarah continued, "as you saw last night when I was ranting about that antacid commercial, we feel very strongly about treating the causes, not the symptoms, and about treating the whole person."

"Sarah," MJ cut in, "I have a question. You keep saying 'we' as you talk about the Center. I know there are other practitioners here, but how many, and what is the relationship? It is your Center, isn't it?"

"Yes, it is my Center, MJ. I guess you could call me the founding partner, and I do own a majority of the company. So, bottom line, the buck does stop here, and if a tough decision needs to be made, I'll be the one that has to make it. But I firmly believe that the collective wisdom of all of us is much greater than just mine.

And that a company that has its people participate in the planning and execution of its future provides for ownership, partnership and what I would call 'broad leadership' as opposed to 'point' leadership, which tends to concentrate the power and decision making in just a few places."

"Sarah," I exclaimed, "I remember you getting your Naturopathic degree and then finishing your MD requirements in Minnesota at the Mayo Clinic, and I know you studied in lots of clinics around the world. But I don't remember you getting any degrees in management or organizational development."

She blushed ever so slightly. "I have been doing my homework, Jack. You can't start or run a business, or manage people, without spending at least some time trying to figure out the best and most effective way to do it."

"Right, right," I said softly, thinking that I sure hadn't spent much time lately thinking about that stuff.

"Anyway," Sarah continued, "let me give you the rundown on the partners at the Center. Let's see," Sarah bit her lip in that way I had always found so engaging, "there are eight of us. Virender, our Ayurvedic doctor; Renee, our massage therapist; our chiropractor Teresa; Li, our Chinese herbalist; Jacquie, our Reiki Master; Al, our psychologist; me, with my degrees and training in both naturopathic and allopathic medicine; and Nancy, our office administrator."

"Sounds like quite a team, Sarah," Elton commented.

"They are, and I am sure you'll like them. Let's see if we can find some of them now, and the rest you can meet at the dinner tonight."

We headed out of the "Gathering Place" and met a few of the partners who weren't engaged with visitors. Then Sarah steered us down the hall.

"Let me show you one of our care rooms," she said. She opened a door and led us in. It was nothing like the doctor rooms

I'd been in. There was color on the walls, soft lighting, and a calm, soothing feel.

"Wow! This is nice. Really nice," MJ exclaimed.

"Thanks," Sarah said. "We really have worked hard to get our rooms to feel like a home. We want our patients to be as relaxed and comfortable as possible, not only for their own well-being, but because a calm, relaxed, patient is more in touch with what they are really feeling, and much more able to express it."

"Your paint job sure doesn't look like the ones I've done," Elton said. "What did you do?"

"Actually my friend Dayna, who is the expert in decorative painting and design, did most of the work. But I helped when I could and I learned quite a bit. Let's see if I remember all the techniques. We color-washed the top half of the wall in an azure tone, and "schmoozed" the lower half in a deeper blue with white tones."

"Excuse me," Elton cut in. "Schmoozed?"

Sarah started to answer but MJ cut in.

"I know what that is. Can I tell him, Sarah?"

"Be my guest," Sarah said. She knew MJ had always liked interior design and decorations.

"Schmoozing," MJ began, " is a technique where you lay clear plastic over fresh paint and schmooze the paint around until you get the color and texture you want. If the color doesn't look right— say it's too dark—you lay a lighter color over it quickly, then schmooze it again. Kind of like mixing your paints on the wall."

"Much better said than I could have done, MJ," Sarah complimented her before continuing. "Dayna recommended some contrast between the blues, so we laid down this off-white textured wallpaper border. Smashing, don't you think? She's quite talented."

I had to agree with that. And the rest of the room was designed with those same themes of comfort and relaxation in mind. The diagnostic table was covered with a soft throw that picked up the colors from the walls. Several Monet prints depicting different views of his garden and lily pond at Giverny adorned the walls. Two nice chairs faced each other in the center of the room so Sarah and the patients could talk to each other comfortably and eye-to-eye. A freesia scented aromatherapy candle burned in the corner, and a small, self-contained waterfall sat on the windowsill gently pouring water into its pebbled pool. Outside the window the sun was shining and flowering shrubs showed off their colorful blossoms.

I looked up. Across the top of the cantilevered wall, just as in the Gathering Place with the vision statement, there was a stenciled phrase. This one said:

IN OLD CHINA, A DOCTOR WAS PAID AS LONG AS THE PATIENT WAS WELL.

"Sarah," I said pointing up, "tell me about the sayings. Do you have them in all the rooms, and what is the particular meaning of this one?"

"Yes, we do have sayings or quotations in all the rooms. I think it tells people about our values and adds meaning to the rooms beyond what the paint and decorations can bring. This particular one is a favorite of mine. It is completely true. Doctors in old China were paid as long as the patient was healthy. If the patient became ill, the doctor would perform all treatment and services free. Now think of that paradigm. You were doing your job, and received compensation for it, when your patients were healthy. So your goal was 100% health for everyone in the village. Therefore, you spent a lot of time ensuring that everyone under your care understood healthy behaviors, foods, the importance of rest, joy, and physical activities."

"Now, in the West, if everyone under our care is healthy, doctors get no money. The goal of the patient is to be healthy all the time, yet if the doctor only gets paid when they are ill, then by nature the focus of the doctor isn't on wellness, but on illness and disease. They, literally, have to hope for sickness or they go broke. Now that's goofy. And our insurance companies promote this, often refusing to pay for many inexpensive preventative measures, like physicals, wellness visits, stress reducers like yoga and meditation, certain tests for disease, regular massage, and so on—yet they routinely pay a hundred or even a thousand times those amounts for heart attack care, serious illness care, back surgeries, and joint or organ replacements." She paused and smiled sheepishly. "Sorry, preaching a little."

"I don't mind you preaching," I said. "I always learn when you get on your soapbox." She smiled again as I continued. "But I do have one question, and don't answer if it is too personal. I'm thinking it must have been pretty costly to get the Center off the ground, what with the building and equipment, insurance and the like. How could you afford these expensive decorations and furnishings?"

"Honestly, it wasn't all that expensive. Most of it was just labor. The most expensive thing was the waterfall. Self-contained units like that run about a hundred on sale. The chairs we got at garage sales and thrift shops, cleaned them thoroughly and recovered them ourselves. The real difficulty in doing a room like this lies in the knowledge of how to do the painting, papering, and Feng Shui, and the eye to put it all together. Dayna did that for us and we traded her services for some healthcare and massages."

"Fung what?" Elton said.

"Feng Shui." She pronounced it Fung Schway. "It's the Chinese art of arranging your surroundings so they promote peace, well-being, and harmony. I am not entirely sure how or why it works, but I do feel great in the Center."

"Me too," Elton said. "This is a wonderful place. Think you could open one in Phoenix?"

She laughed. "Not any time soon, Elton my boy. This one was hard enough to keep any thoughts of opening satellite offices out of my head."

From the front, discussions and laughter wafted back to us. Sarah glanced that way.

"I've got to go. Look around and I'll be back in a while. Check today's schedule, also. I'm sure one of the other partners will be doing a lecture or demonstration soon." And she was off.

We wandered around a while, and did indeed catch a talk by Virender on Ayruvedic medicine, an old—5000 years—eastern Indian tradition that emphasizes balancing, feeding and internally cleansing the body, as well as breathing and fitness. We met Sarah's parents there as they listened in, and got to spend a few minutes talking with them after Virender was done. They seemed very proud of Sarah, and a tear formed in the corner of my eye as I remembered Sarah's letter to them when she had left her residency. She had specifically stated that she hoped one day they would be proud of her and what she was doing in healing. Today they seemed very proud. They were glowing, and so was Sarah.

Shortly thereafter, they closed the Center to the public and began to set up for the dinner. Sarah's parents headed off to their hotel—they had graciously offered to stay in one so as not to break up the four of us—to clean up and change after their long day flying and participating in the grand opening. We helped set up the tables and chairs in the Gathering Place, grabbed some refreshments and lounged around waiting for the action to start.

chapter **eleven**

I paused in my storytelling and took stock of myself. I felt fine, no pain, no discomfort. I wasn't tired and I wasn't hungry. All in all, I thought, I was feeling pretty good. Especially for someone who apparently has had a brush with death, and whose only communication is with a disembodied voice that seems to know an awful lot about me. I listened for that voice but heard nothing.

"Sandor, you napping or just visiting Captain Kirk in the Delta Quadrant?"

"Neither," Sandor said with a chuckle. "Just waiting for my human friend to continue with his story."

"Aha," I announced triumphantly. "So *you* aren't human!"

"I didn't say that, Jack. I only made the obvious observation: that you are human."

"Yes," I said softly. I wasn't ready to give up yet. "But by calling me human, you are saying that I am alive and still human. Because if I were dead and you were an angel or something, I would no longer be human, I would be an angel too, or a spirit, or ..."

"A little devil," Sandor said, trying to keep his voice serious but losing the battle and erupting in laughter.

"Hey, hey, that's not nice." I hesitated. "There aren't really devils out there, are there?"

"Humans are so curious," Sandor mused. "Okay. If you will continue on with your story, I will answer your question. Agreed?"

"Agreed," I said.

"All right. In my experience, Jack, there are no devils. Now let's continue."

"Wait, wait. 'In your experience?' What's that supposed to mean? What is your experience? Are you just guessing?"

"It is not time for you to know these things. Now, I have answered your question truthfully. It is time you kept your end of the bargain."

Damn, this guy was a good negotiator. "Okay, let's continue with Sarah's wellness center. We were all hanging out in the Gathering Place waiting for her to finish her good-byes and handle some logistics for the dinner."

"Yes," Sandor said, "that is where you left off. Finish the story, Jack."

Sarah joined us in the Gathering Place a short while later and plopped down on a big throw pillow.

"Whew, it's been a great day so far," she said, "but I'm beat."

"Hey, Sarah," Elton said, "are you too beat to answer a question? I'm intrigued by what you said about using the collective wisdom of the organization. Would you mind expanding on that, and maybe give me your thoughts on how you might do that?"

Good question, I thought to myself. I could use some advice on that. It perked Sarah up, also.

"Thanks for reminding me, Elton," she said as she jumped up. "I have a little time left before dinner and I've been meaning to show all of you a tool I learned that has really helped to view cases from all sides and allow everyone to participate." She started pulling some of the easels from the corners of the room and taping some pages to the wall. "I knew I needed to have more than just me thinking about the business, and that each of us would benefit from sharing our knowledge about our patients and possible diagnoses and courses of action. So, my first step was to set up the environment—a culture where sharing and new ideas were valued, and where people felt free to speak their minds. I had to set the tone for that, provide positive reinforcement, and encourage everyone to participate. Then I went looking for tools that would further that environment and help us to be more effi-

cient in sharing knowledge, analyzing data, and making decisions. That's when I found The Six Thinking Hats."

"The Six Thinking Hats?" Elton echoed. "I don't think I have
heard of that."

"It is a new tool developed by Dr. Edward de Bono," Sarah
said as she taped up the final chart.

'Now I have heard of him," Elton said. "He is quite well
known for his work on thinking and creativity, isn't he?"

"Exactly," Sarah replied. "And..."

"Whoa," MJ cut in, "Edward de what? Who's that?"

"Edward de Bono," Sarah replied. "As Elton said, he is known
for his work in thinking and creativity. He studied the mind from
all aspects, receiving an MD, Ph.D., and a Rhodes scholarship in
the process. His book *The Mechanism of Mind* was published in
1970 and detailed how the mind worked, including a section on
neural networks in the brain that was far ahead of its time. He
decided to concentrate his career on helping people think better
and more creatively. Thinking is a skill, he said, therefore if one
had tools and techniques to improve that skill, thinking would
improve. This is just like an athlete who possesses some amount
of talent, but given better techniques, training aids and so forth,
can become much better. His point is that the mind works the
same. We all have some degree of innate intelligence, but we can
all get more skillful at using it if we learn how. He has devoted his
life to the study and communication of thinking and creativity."

"Wow," MJ said. "He sounds like one smart dude. Has he written any more books?"

Sarah laughed. "About forty more. He's very prolific. But he
has really concentrated on two areas. One is children. They are
the future, he believes—and rightly so, I might add—and we
don't teach them thinking skills. Math, history, science—all good
things to learn—but we don't teach them how to use the mind
more effectively, or how to be more creative. So de Bono invent-
ed CoRT, a program to teach kids how to think and be more

creative. It can be used at home, or put into the kindergarten through high school curriculum. I think quite a few countries around the world have added it to their schools."

"What does CoRT stand for," I asked. "It is an acronym, isn't it?"

"Yes, it is," Sarah replied slowly, her eyes rolling back as she searched her memory. "I think it stands for Cognitive Research Tools or something like that. It is not an intuitive acronym, that's for sure."

"I'll say," I laughed. "You mentioned that de Bono focused on two areas. What's the other?"

"Business. He believes that if children are the future, then business and industry are the present, so to speak. They must solve many of the pressing concerns we have now. His tool kit to support business is impressive, and includes The Six Thinking Hats. That's what we have started using here. De Bono developed The Six Thinking Hats as a thinking framework, and to promote 'full color thinking.' That's a term that means that the thinker, or group of thinkers, is considering all aspects and sides of an issue.

"Okay," Sarah continued, "let me show you how we use Six Hats here at the Center." She pointed to the walls, liberally decorated with large flip chart paper. "Here is a 'Six Hats history' of one of our patients. She gave me permission to talk about her case to demonstrate how we treat people, as well as some of the tools we use, like Six Hats. Of course, I've changed the names for the demonstration.

"As you know, this is the grand opening of the Center, but, like many businesses, we planned the grand opening to be a few months after our initial opening. This gave us a chance to work out some bugs, finish the painting and decorations, get all the staff here, and let the community see and hear about us for a while before we invited them to join us for the grand opening. And right after we opened, in came Flo." Sarah smiled in recollection. "Or perhaps I should say, in came Paul dragging Flo.

"Flo appeared nervous and not at all pleased to be there. Paul was her son, well dressed, mid-forties, appeared to be in pretty good shape, although certainly looking stressed and worried that day. He told Nancy he wanted to see me right away."

"*He* wanted to see you?" MJ asked puzzled. "I thought Flo was the patient."

"She was," Sarah answered, "but he wanted to tell me all about it before I saw Flo. Nancy showed him to a care room. The one good thing about having a new clinic is that you can work with walk-ins right away. I came in and introduced myself and held out my hand. He took it, but as he did I could see he was giving me a quick once-over. He tried to be polite about it but I could see he was sizing me up and wondering if I was up to the job he had in mind.

"I asked him what was troubling him and he said it wasn't him, it was his mom. He was worried about her and wanted to give me some information about what he saw going on in her life before I saw her. He hesitated a few seconds, then put his head down and covered his face with his hands. When he looked up his eyes were full of pain as well as tears.

'I feel like she's trying to kill herself,' he said.

"When I pressed him for more details, he admitted that she hadn't overtly tried to harm herself, but that she just didn't seem to care about her health or wellness. He listed a whole raft of things that she did—or didn't—do. Things like smoking, drinking, chugging coffee, taking sleeping pills, no exercise, poor diet, and no social life or desire to meet people and build relationships. He felt like her habits were so destructive that it was as good as a death sentence.

"I thanked him and invited Flo in. I asked her how she was feeling. Her answer was telling."

'Fine, I suppose. I'm a little tired and my back aches, but I guess that's normal for a sixty year old.'

"Referring to her age as an excuse for feeling poorly was a consistent theme. Of course, we all know many sixty, seventy, eighty, or even ninety year-olds who exude energy, joy and spirit. They are active in the community, have a good social life, many hobbies, and look forward to each day. Flo wasn't there yet. I asked her if there were any significant events in her life the last few years. She hesitated, but finally told me about her second husband and their divorce several years earlier.

"It was a long marriage and he was very controlling, she said, and she felt as though she had began to lose her self identity. She quit her career to support his business and when he left her suddenly—after twenty years—and treated her like a business negotiation, not a long time lover and partner during the divorce, she fell apart. Everyone expected her to bounce back quickly, especially Paul, but she hadn't been able to.

"As we talked I learned that she also spent a good deal of time worrying about the future, not only money and such, but also about running into her ex or his friends and wondering what they would think. She tended to focus externally and on what others thought of her, as opposed to internally and on doing what was right for her mentally, emotionally, and spiritually. She really had no belief in her own value and it is from that that she picked up destructive habits and couldn't—or more accurately, wouldn't—get rid of them. I asked her why she continued with these destructive habits.

"'Well, I'm sixty years old and I've had these habits for a long time. You just can't break them at my age.'

"'Do you really believe that?' I asked.

"She hesitated, wanting to say yes and stick to her position, but knowing that it wasn't true. Finally, she said in a halting voice. 'It seems too hard. I don't have any will power any more. I wish I could change some of these habits, but I'm just not strong enough.'

"'I think you are, Flo,' I told her. We talked about some of her physical symptoms, which included fatigue, respiratory issues, backaches, as well as frequent colds and flu, then we scheduled her for some tests and a return visit.

"So that is how my conversation went with Paul and Flo," Sarah said. Now let me show you how we used The Six Thinking

Hats to support our work. At the end of the day our team gathered for the daily p.m. stand-up. Yes, you heard right, Jack. We have daily stand-ups, two in fact, one first thing in the morning and one as we wrap things up for the day. Just as in our new business proposal days at Dynamics, we start the day with a short meeting. We go over who is coming in for the day, and make sure we are all in sync. At the afternoon stand-up, we go over what happened that day and share cases to make sure we get input from all our minds, instead of just the primary healer."

"Now that," I cut in, "sounds pretty unrealistic. I can't believe you have the time to do that kind of sharing on every case you treat each day."

"You're right there," Sarah agreed. "So we have set guidelines. We go over every new case, and each case where there is significant change."

"That still sounds like a huge time commitment," I said. "How are you going to run enough patients through there to really make money if you have to spend all your time de-briefing each other?"

Sarah smiled a bit wistfully. "Ah, there's the Jack I know and love. First off, it isn't all about money. Second..."

"I know, I know," I cut in quickly, sensing my gaffe. "I just meant..."

"I know what you meant," Sarah cut back in, "and you are right in that we have to make money or we will go out of business and help no one. But our focus is on *quality* help to people, and that does take a little more time. But in terms of our afternoon stand-ups, Six Hats really helps us be more focused, reduce conflict, and do parallel thinking instead of adversarial thinking. And that saves a lot of time."

"Hold on," Elton cut in. "Parallel thinking and..."

Sarah held up her hand. "Hang on to that question; we'll get to that in a minute. Let me start by giving you a rundown on what the Hats are about."

Sarah pointed to a wall chart that had six colored hats on them with brief descriptions underneath. "There are six hats, as the title suggests, and each signifies a certain aspect of thinking.

"The white hat is the facts and data hat. Devoted to what you know, what you need to know, and how you get it. Think Joe Friday of Dragnet—'Just the facts, ma'am.'

"The red hat represents emotions, intuition, feelings. Important ingredients in thinking that are often overlooked, especially in western society where we value logic and critical thinking, and discount feelings and emotions.

"Black hat looks at concerns, problems and issues, but they must be logical, and reasons must be given as to why something is a concern or issue. If it is just negative without any logic, then it would be red hat, that person's feelings."

"So," Elton interjected laughing, "when Maire says 'Elton, that idea will never work,' she has her red hat on."

"Exactly," Sarah smiled. "And if she says 'that will never work because you need fifty thousand dollars to implement it and you only have five,' that's the logical concern and would be black hat. Knowing Maire's brains and intuition, she would probably be right either way."

Elton nodded ruefully, a smile creasing his face.

"Anyway," Sarah turned back to the chart, "the yellow hat is really the opposite of the black. You might call it the logical positive. It focuses on the benefits of the situation or proposal.

"The green hat is the creativity hat. It opens up time and space for creative thinking. A micro-culture, a micro-climate of creativity can be created where ideas, alternatives, and possibilities are generated. A powerful way to use the green hat is after the black hat, to overcome the concerns that have been raised.

"And the last one here is the blue hat. It is the process control hat. While the other hats are thinking about the issue or proposal, the blue hat is thinking about the thinking. 'How are things going?' 'Do we need more green hat here?' 'Is it time to move to the black hat?' Also, prior to the meeting, the facilitator or team leader wears the blue hat to plan the meeting."

"So, that sounds interesting," I said, "but how do you actually use the hats?"

"Well, in a general business sense, the hats can be inserted during a conversation or meeting as in, 'We need some fresh ideas, let's do three minutes of green hat thinking.' Or a whole meeting can be planned with a specific sequence of hats developed and followed to ensure a full-color exploration of the subject. Now, I'll show you how we use them here at the Center in our stand-ups, and as we do that, I think you will be able to see how our concept of treating the whole person—not just the parts—and being open to alternative therapies, works.

"On the day Flo visited we all gathered in the 'Gathering Place' for the afternoon stand-up."

"Do you really have to stand up?" Elton cracked. "Do you have to go to the penalty box if you sit down or what?"

Sarah shook her head as she smiled.

"Actually, we do often sit. 'Stand-up' is just a conceptual notion of a quick, no-nonsense meeting." She looked over at Elton. "Unlike this one."

"Ouch," he said, "I won't interrupt any more. Promise." He crossed the air in front of his chest and mouthed, "cross my heart and hope to die."

Sarah rolled her eyes and continued.

"So, there we were at the afternoon stand-up. There were only six of us that day—Virender, Renee, Li, Al, me, and Nancy, our office administrator. Jacquie and Teresa were still in the process of closing their old locations and moving in to ours."

"No disrespect intended," MJ began, "but if you are going over treatments and so forth, why do you include your office administrator?"

"That's a fair question, MJ. We include Nancy not only to make the point that our team really is a team, but more importantly, as a non-medical person, she enters our meetings with an entirely different viewpoint. She helps remind us what it is like to be a patient, to be on the other side of the table, so to speak. She pops us out of our paradigms sometimes and helps us come up with new and better treatment plans. Edward de Bono calls this 'popping' lateral thinking, a concept and set of tools that we can discuss later if you all want.

"So, there we were, the six of us. I quickly outlined the hat sequence for Flo's case. Sequencing is the order you put the hats in; different sequences are better for different purposes. We put the data and ideas we generate on flipcharts, and the ones for Flo are on the wall here. In Six Hat terminology, I was wearing the Blue Hat to lead and focus the thinking process." Sarah pointed to the first flipchart.

"We started with the white hat, as we usually do, so everyone has a common understanding of the facts and data on the case. I briefly described my visit with Paul and his concerns, then turned to Flo. Now, since I was the only one who talked to her, I told everyone what I knew and wrote it on the flipchart. They asked questions and I answered and continued to quickly write."

WHITE HAT
INFORMATION, FACTS, AND DATA

• 60 years old • traumatic divorce 3 years ago • smokes • drinks • takes sleeping pills • eats poorly	• does not exercise • drinks no water • drinks 6-8 cups of coffee a day • symptoms: fatigue, backaches, pre-emphysema, prone to colds and flu, constipated

"We discussed the white hat data, then I moved us on to the green hat and asked for everyone's ideas on a treatment plan. Nancy actually jumped in first and said, 'I think she's lonely and needs to be touched. Let's start with a massage and see if we can help the backaches, and fill her 'touch well' a little.'" Sarah pointed to the next flipchart on the wall.

"Here are the possibilities we generated. You can see that they are pretty varied. At this point we want all the ideas we can get; we don't judge them here. In creative sessions, quantity breeds quality, so we encourage everyone to throw any thoughts and possibilities out on the table."

"Sarah," Elton interrupted, "if you don't mind, could you quickly explain why quantity breeds quality. In other areas that isn't true. Like in baseball, a bunch of bad players doesn't turn into a few good ones."

"Sure," Sarah said. "The key thing to understand is that the mind is a self-organizing patterning system."

"Oh, that explains it," MJ cut in. "I got it now. No problem. The old self-organizing patterning system. Should have thought of that myself."

Sarah laughed. "It's not as bad as it sounds, MJ. All it means is that the mind organizes all the experiences and knowledge it receives so that you can function efficiently and effectively in life—and stay alive. For example, once you learn to tie your shoes, you no longer have to think about how to do it. You just do it. When you drive a car and you come to a traffic signal, you know that red means stop, green means go, and yellow means..."

"Go faster!" MJ interjected.

"Right," Sarah laughed again. "So, in terms of being creative, it is hard for you to break out of the old patterns that are entrenched in your mind. Have you ever been in a meeting where you were asked to come up with some new ideas, and all that came out were the same old ideas?" I was nodding my head rapidly. That happened all the time at Dynamics.

"Well," Sarah continued, "it is because the mind is accessing all its organized data, and of course none of that is new or different. Think of the mind in this sense as a valley. You are traveling down the valley road and this is the route the mind knows. It doesn't see any alternative roads because down in the valley it can't. But what if you somehow popped up to the hillside? Now you can see many roads to the destination.

"So, the key question is, how do we help the mind get to the hillside so lots of alternatives and possibilities can be seen? One way is to use the lateral thinking tools I mentioned earlier. Another way—and this gets back to the question of why quantity breeds quality with idea generation—is to allow all the ideas, some of which might be crazy or unworkable in their present form, to pop us out of our valley and get us looking at things from a different perspective. And since all our valleys are different, each idea will affect each of us differently. So the more chances we have to trigger us to new ideas—or to build on ideas—the better. And, by the way, that is why diversity is so important. A group that has lots of different valleys in terms of experience, culture, education and so on will trigger much more robust and diverse idea generation sessions."

"Wow, that is cool stuff," MJ said. "I would love to learn more about it."

"I'll tell you all I know whenever you want MJ," Sarah replied. "But I'm no expert."

"Sounds like you're enough of an expert for me. And I can't wait to hear about all those lateral thinking tools you mentioned."

Sarah nodded and smiled, then turned back to the Green Hat flipchart on the wall.

GREEN HAT	
IDEAS, POSSIBILITIES, & ALTERNATIVES	
• needs to be touched-start with massage • smoking cessation program • counseling—she needs to release her ex-husband • Chinese herbs to promote sleep and reduce dependencies on pills	• AA • nutrition plan • exercise plan • food and drink diary • she needs confidence, start with something she can succeed at and build from there

After we'd looked that over Sarah continued.

"Then I asked for their gut feelings, their instincts on what the best start-up treatments were for Flo. You see the choices we made on this red hat chart."

RED HAT *FEELINGS, EMOTIONS, & INTUITION*	• massage • counseling • food diary • confidence –start with success

"Next, we did a yellow/black hat assessment of each alternative. That simply means that we looked at the benefits, the value of an idea—the yellow hat, then at the potential problems, issues, and concerns—the black hat. Our thinking is shown here."

"So, *all* of you generate the yellow and black hat for each alternative?" I asked.

YELLOW HAT *Logical Positives, Benefits*	BLACK HAT *Logical Concerns, Problems*
Massage • she'll feel love • backache better • get blood circulating • she'll leave relaxed and feel immediate benefit	**Massage** • backache may have non-muscular (e.g. emotional or structural) cause
Counseling • may get to root cause of problem • she clearly needs to release issues and treat herself better	**Counseling** • may take a while to see results
Food Diary • not passive - she can take active part • need to find out what's really going on nutritionally	**Food Diary** • she may not do it accurately, or at all
Confidence - Start with Success • she needs a success	**Confidence - Start with Success** • no concerns

"That's right, Jack, and you can see some of the power of Six Hats thinking here. Instead of each of us 'defending' our particular proposal, we *together* look at the benefits of each idea, and *together* look at the concerns. We're not thinking the same thing; we're thinking *about* the same thing." Sarah nodded over to Elton. "Dr. de Bono calls this parallel thinking—as opposed to adversarial thinking—and it really promotes getting the full power and use of every mind present. It tends to separate one's ego from the discussion."

"Wow, we could use that at Dynamics. We have a lot of ego present, and a lot of 'defending our turf' goes on. It would be great to have a tool that really helps get a fairer and fuller look at all sides of an issue."

"Exactly," Sarah said. "That would be especially important in corporate settings where ego and defending the status quo often get in the way of new ideas and breakthrough thinking. At least it did all those years ago when I was in Dynamics."

"Oh, it's still that way," I said ruefully. "Trust me on that one."

"So how do you end one of these meetings Sarah? Which hat is that?" Elton asked.

"Blue hat, Elton. That hat summarizes, outlines next steps and makes decisions. In Flo's case, we made some decisions as to treatment and then summarized our plan.

BLUE HAT
NEXT STEPS, DECISIONS, & SUMMARIES

Decisions:

- need a success—so start with food diary
- get commitment for three glasses of water a day—as she notes drinking them in diary she will feel success
- counseling a must
- massage will be good for her body and soul

Next Steps:

- start food and water diary
- start multi-vitamin and mineral capsule
- start counseling
- schedule massage—twice weekly
- keep Paul informed, calm, and supportive
- re-visit with team in one month

"Because of the nature and extent of Flo's issues, we agreed on multiple treatments. Other times we might pick only one; or sometimes we feel as though we don't have enough white hat data and then we assign action to collect more data and return to the group."

"Okay, Sarah, this looks great," I said. "But how long did it take? With all this output, it still must have taken too long to be cost effective."

"You be the judge, Jack. It took eleven minutes and thirty-eight seconds. I know, because we recognized early on that we had to get all the minds and spirits involved if we were to truly heal in the best way possible; and yet if we spent too much time we couldn't pay the bills. So we learned tools like the Six Thinking Hats, and then Nancy timed each case so we could measure our time expenditure and try to improve it. So that first session on Flo was only 11 minutes and thirty-eight seconds. That's still a lot if you had ten of these a day. But as I mentioned earlier, we don't do each patient in the full group each visit. As you saw on the blue hat with Flo, we recommended re-visiting in a month. This cuts down the load, while still involving all our healing power. And if more frequent reviews are necessary, we do them.

"Also, we are getting better at using the tools and making decisions. A beginning review of a case very similar to Flo's last week took six minutes and forty-two seconds. So I know that we're getting more and more efficient."

"That's pretty impressive, Sarah girl," Elton said affectionately. "But now I'm curious about Flo. Can you tell us what happened?"

"Well, it's only been a few months since we started, but here's what happened so far. When Flo returned for her next appointment, I went over our treatment plan with her. I explained each part to her, and why our staff thought it would work. I've had some people question our policy of explaining each treatment and why. They think that disclosing some of our 'soft,' less 'scientific' reasons for treatment might scare off some patients who are used to a western, scientific reason, or no reason at all. I haven't found that to be the case. Patients may ask questions about what and why, but they seem to understand and appreciate our non-surgical and non-drug based remedies. For example, when I told Flo we were recommending massage because we thought it would make her back feel better, help release the stress, and because we felt she needed to be touched and feel connected to another person, she just looked at me then nodded. And she's been here on time for every session.

"After two months of following our treatment plan, the white hat data was that she was feeling better, successfully keeping a food diary, drinking two to three glasses of water daily, sleeping better, reducing her prescription sleeping pills and her coffee intake, but still smoking and not yet exercising.

"The yellow hat benefits of her treatment that Flo has reported are more sustained energy, reduced constipation, back feels much better, and she is not dwelling on her ex-husband as much.

"The black hat concerns we or Flo have are that her smoking is very ingrained and her motivation to quit seems very low, she isn't exercising, her coffee intake is still too high, and she is still taking addictive prescription drugs to sleep.

"Flo is going to continue counseling and Al—our psychologist—is really encouraging her to build on her initial success. This week she started a walking program, and is determined to cut her coffee down to a couple cups a day and increase her water consumption. She says she is also going to stop the addictive sleeping pills. She is focusing on her diet as a key to how she feels physically each day, and we have recommended a better balance in carbohydrate, protein, and fat, and more consistent eating to keep a steady energy level. We built a food plan to help her with that. We also decided not to tackle quitting smoking at this time, that she needed more successes first, more confidence. When we do get to that, we will recommend acupuncture as that seems to help with addictions."

"Good for Flo," MJ said. "I really admire someone having the courage to change after all those setbacks and all those years of doing things a certain way. I think I'll send my mom to see you,

Sarah. She's in kind of a rut herself and could stand to break some bad habits and get her old energy back."

"So, Sarah," I cut in, "how would you sum up your philosophy here, your blue hat, I guess, on what you are trying to do?"

"Well, our vision is our cornerstone and there it is on the wall again."

Treat the whole body, mind and spirit of our patients to promote wellness and prevent and/or heal illness and injury.

"From a more tactical point of view, in our healing process we focus on successes, then build on them. We definitely try to look at a case from all angles and all possible types of healing. If something isn't working we try others, to include allopathic medicine. We all try to check our egos at the door and look for any way possible to help the patient. We treat the whole body and the mind, and are very conscious that the fuel (food) we put in our bodies has a huge effect on how we function, both short and long term.

"Also, having a wonderful, supportive working environment is such a joy. I love and respect the staff and their families. We spend time together outside of work doing community service or just playing. At the Center we work hard, take breaks for tea and mental stimulation, and also take some quiet time. We feel that makes us more responsive to our patients and brings enlighten-ment. It is such a wonderful assembly of individuals and we make a great team. It shows you what a little intent to the Universe will bring. We are making a difference. We are *caring* for our patients in the truest sense of the word."

"That is so great, Sarah," MJ said. "Congratulations on your success and on following both your passion and your dreams. I admire your drive and your courage."

I stopped my story. I was stuck on that last line of MJ's, espe-cially the admiration of Sarah's courage. I admired her courage, too. Maybe even envied it. I had forgotten all she had overcome to start her Center. To stand up for what she wanted to do against convention, culture and family history, and then to have the brains, emotional intelligence and courage to see it through. And to have as your ultimate goal helping people, helping the community, helping the world. I wasn't sure I had the courage to take those types of steps at Dynamics—to do the right things, for the right people, for the right reasons, at the right time.

I sighed. It felt like déjà vu. I had learned this before. Why hadn't it stuck? I had a strong recollection of standing alone in the clinic and wondering if I would use my new knowledge of hats and hearts, of courage and caring. I had turned to find Sarah staring at me from the doorway with a curious and almost sad look on her face. She had cocked her head thoughtfully and slipped out the door. Surely she couldn't read minds, too?

"Jack," Sandor said softly, "you've stopped your story."

"I know," I replied. "I'm sorry." I tried to refocus. "Where was I?"

"It was the night before your conversation with Sarah."

"Right. Let me get back to it."

The rest of the evening, the dinner and so forth, was a blur. I was already thinking about tomorrow. What would I say to Sarah, and was I ready to have a conversation about my "path?" As the time drew near for me to actually be with her one-on-one, I could feel the fear close in. This was too much openness for me. What would I say to her? This path stuff was way too nebulous. I was used to numbers and facts and deadlines, and I knew that wasn't where we would be focused tomorrow. As I slipped into bed that night, I was entertaining thoughts of getting up early and heading for the airport. In my position, it was easy to claim a work emergency and be gone in an instant. But I didn't. I lay in bed and worked on my courage. I knew it was time to tackle not only the path issue, but also the Sarah issue. If I ran every time we had an opportunity to spend quality time together, I had no chance for any kind of meaningful relationship. "So be it," I said to myself. "Let's roll the dice tomorrow."

In the morning, Sarah and I loaded MJ and Elton into my rental car and drove them to the airport. After the drop-off, we headed to Pike Place market where I got introduced to something called a latte. It was sort of like a cappuccino, but not exactly. Sarah said the company that had made them popular in the Northwest was called Starbucks, and they were starting to go national and even international.

"You might think about picking up a few shares of their stock when they go public," she said. "I'm going to."

"How can you make money selling little coffee drinks?" I asked. "Especially when you can get a good solid 'cup of Joe' for less than half the cost of one of these. I see 'fad' written all over this."

"We'll see," she said. "My intuition tells me otherwise. I'm a tea drinker normally, but even I like to have one of these special-ty type coffees once in a while."

I nodded, taking a sip. It was good, I had to admit. My mind only stayed there for a few seconds, though. I was nervous about our talk, and I had been looking for a way to casually slip into it ever since we dropped off MJ and Elton. I hadn't seen any open-ings, however, and I knew if I didn't get it going I might lose my nerve altogether. I took a deep breath, bringing the cup up to hide my face. I let the breath out slowly and turned to Sarah as we walked past the market tables full of fresh fruits and vegetables.

"Okay, Sarah, I have a question for you. You said in your note that I had helped you find your true path. How did I do that? Frankly, I'd like to take credit, but I have no idea what I did."

She looked thoughtful. "You know, Jack, I don't think people usually know when they are helping others down their path. One reason is that *other* people don't know *your* path. They may think they know it, but normally what they know is what they want you to do. Happens a lot to kids as their parents try to push them in the direction they want them to go.

"What you did was offer me a refuge, a place safe from the storm, and an environment I truly loved. I needed that desperately. More than I can tell you. I was making a decision that rocked not only my foundation, but my family's as well. It also threw my finances into turmoil. I was deeply in debt and now had no immediate way to climb out. I was looking at a long road down what I thought was my path, towards a goal I thought I knew, with no apparent means to get there."

"Wow," I muttered. "I never knew you had those kinds of doubts. Even when we talked that day in L.A., you seemed so sure of yourself, so positive of your decision."

"My intuition was strong, but reality was staring me in the face and it didn't care about my intuition. I'm human like everyone else. There were clearly obstacles in my path, and I knew that what I was doing would be condemned by nearly everyone I talked to. I was scared for me, afraid of my family's reactions and uncertain what to do next.

"You, Jack, didn't judge me. You even praised my courage, and then you showed me the next step. Complete with resources like Father Antonio, an inexpensive yet wonderful place to live, even a bathtub I loved that I could sit and soak and plan my future in. You opened the door that allowed me to step onto my path fully and completely."

She suddenly leaned over and kissed me on the cheek.

"For all that, I am eternally grateful. The East/West Holistic Wellness Center would not be here today without you."

I couldn't talk. The kiss, the credit, the closeness...I was in ecstasy—but filled with terror. What should I do now? As I struggled to find the words—or maybe kiss her back—an old sports term came to mind. "Choking." I was choking! Here was my chance, the pressure was on, and if I pulled it off the reward would be incredible. But I was choking so badly, I couldn't even talk. She looked up at me, apparently convinced I had nothing to add or say, and changed the focus.

"What about you, Jack? Have you been giving any thought to your path?"

Talk about intuition. Bingo. She had hit my other subject on the head. I focused my mind on that. My path. That was hard to discuss also, but it felt easy compared to where we just were.

"Actually, I've been thinking about that, Sarah. It was your note and your discussion of your path that got me thinking about it. But, I must confess, my thinking hasn't been particularly constructive. I'm not sure where to start or where to focus."

"I think the right beginning is just to allow it to be a subject of thought, Jack. Make it okay to think about, something that is worth your time. When you do that, the information, internal dialogue, conversations, and resources start to show up. And allow your own intuition to play a part."

I frowned. "I seem to trust my intuition when it comes to business, but in life and relationships, I'm a little wary of it."

"That's natural. Just keep working at it." She paused, biting her lip. "What does your intuition tell you about your path?"

"I'm not sure. It seems like I have always had the feeling that I would be a CEO, that I would lead a major corporation. But then I wonder, is that just ambition? And is that a good thing to have as a path anyway? Especially when I consider what you are doing, or others I know. Actually helping people live, saving lives. That seems like a goal that is worthy of giving a life to; but just being a rich, powerful boss—that doesn't sound as good."

"Don't confuse your perceived value of the worth of a path or a life's pursuit with actual value. All paths work towards the whole, and each of us have different roles to play. In your case, you can do so much good. You influence tens of thousands of people directly, and many more indirectly. If you do the right things for the people, the environment, the community, you will affect the planet in a powerful and positive way."

"And if I do the wrong things..."

She shrugged. "I have confidence in you, Jack. Just the fact that you are considering these issues is a great first step."

"Okay, but doing the right things for the people, the environment, and the community doesn't really sound like my job description. That's more like: keep the customers happy and make a pile of money."

"Do they have to be mutually exclusive? I would think one would lead to the other. That's my plan at the Center anyway. To let excited, happy employees and clear value statements lead the way towards success."

"Sure," I replied hastily, "that's okay for a teeny clinic, but I've got a big company to run and..." I looked up at that moment and saw Sarah glaring at me. Damn, I'd stepped in it again. "I didn't mean your clinic wasn't important, I just..." She cut me off.

"Jack, you have a bad habit of being so focused on your own work and goals that you minimize other people's work..."

"But, but..." I tried to cut in.

"...their dreams, and ultimately their lives."

"I didn't mean it that way," I stuttered.

"I know you didn't mean it in a negative way, but let me assure you, it sounds negative when you hear it."

"I'm sorry, Sarah, really I am. I would never do anything to hurt you. I think you're wonderful, I want to be..." I stopped as I realized I was about to blurt out all my feelings about her.

"Be where, Jack?"

I breathed a sigh of relief as I realized she had missed where my last remark had been headed. It wasn't where I wanted to be, it was *who* I wanted to be with...

"Oh, nothing, Sarah, please accept my apologies." I held my watch up. "Wow, look at the time. I'd better be getting back to pack and head off to the airport."

Sarah was looking at me funny but allowed me to take her hand and start her towards the car. We didn't talk much on the way to her house or while I packed, but as we said goodbye near my car, she held up her hand stopping my entry into the driver's seat.

"Jack, I need to get a few thoughts out before you go. First, we never finished our discussion about your path. I'd like to continue that in more depth sometime soon, but for now I have one idea I want to leave with you. You have seen your path as being a CEO in a large corporation, but you wonder if it is just ambition telling you that, not true guidance about your path. You also wonder if things like true concern about employees, community service, and helping the larger good of the planet are really the roles of a major corporation. What if your intuition about your path is accurate, and your life lesson is to get past the ambition and power piece of it, and show that a truly great CEO builds large profits and delights customers *through* focusing on the people, community, environment, and the planet? In other words, those are not just altruistic philosophies—in this day and age they inspire the workforce, build tremendous good will, and lead to long term, sustainable growth and profits."

I nodded slowly. This message sounded familiar. Sarah eased me into the car and leaned over.

"The second thing is about us." I dropped the keys and banged my knee on the steering wheel as I reached for them. Damn, why couldn't I be a little smoother around Sarah?

"You can be irritating, stubborn, obtuse, and even demeaning..."

"Thanks for the compliments," I managed to say.

"...but, we always have a good time together, and our discussions seem to be getting so much richer and more meaningful. I think we ought to do this more often. What do you think?"

"Well, uh, uh..."

"If you're too busy, though..."

"...yes," I finally blurted out in answer to her first question, but it came out right after the second, unfortunately.

"I understand," she said quickly.

"No, no, not that, I mean, yes, I'd love to do this more, and no, I am not too busy." Sweat was breaking out on my forehead, and my whole body felt hot.

"Wonderful," she said. "And let me know your thoughts on your path. It seems to me that you can make a big contribution to your company and the world, Jack."

Sarah reached both hands into the car. Now I wished I were still outside the car so I could give her a hug. I wiped my hands on my pants and grasped them. Sarah's hands were cool and warm at the same time and felt heavenly.

"Goodbye," I said, and Sarah nodded and smiled. I drove off and stopped as soon as I turned the corner. I wiped my brow, took a deep breath and leaned back against the seat, exhaling loudly. Being a good CEO, and being good enough for Sarah. I had a lot of work to do.

chapter **twelve**

"Jack, your story is getting quite interesting, wouldn't you say?"
Sandor said.

"I suppose so," I replied. "Love, business, money, tough decisions. That makes for interesting, if somewhat stressful times."

"Did you return from Seattle and act on some of the new
tools and leadership principles you and Sarah talked about, or
on your relationship with Sarah?"

"Well, no," I said defensively, "but I really couldn't. The
next morning the 'show cause' meetings that I had scheduled
for my return started."

"And those were important?" he questioned.

"Extremely. The importance to Dynamics can't be overstat-
ed. If the contract was canceled for poor performance, our
reputation would be badly damaged, making future contract
wins much harder. Other current contracts were sure to be
scrutinized more closely for signs that we weren't performing,
and a snowball effect could be the start of unhappy customers
and 'bad letters' to us. Also, monetarily, we would not only lose
the profit from the canceled contract, but we would be liable
for the money the government used to 'correct' our deficiencies
with another contractor."

"So you needed to work?"

"Yes, and work hard. And I know what you're thinking. Did
I really have to work that hard, or was this a convenient distraction so I wouldn't have to think about all the hard issues my trip
to Seattle had surfaced? I'll admit it was kind of a convenient
distraction, but it was a defensible one. I mean, we did have a
serious problem on our hands."

"So when you handled that crisis did you turn back to those issues and challenges from Seattle?"

Damn, I thought. This isn't going well at all. "Not exactly," I said. "'Show cause' fights last a while and I also had to go to a mandatory two-week executive training. Those are like boot camp, eighteen hours a day, no outside interaction and future promotions depend on doing well there. And when you get back from that you are behind at work, on your mail, everything."

"I see."

Damn, damn, damn, I thought again. When I looked at it like this, it was clear that once again I had been distracted away from important business in my life. Living life on earth with its obligations and pressures can be hard, and it takes dedication and commitment and is honorable. But what is really hard is facing those questions of life, and spirit, and purpose. That takes courage and vision and is indispensable to one's journey. So far it was clear that both my courage and vision were lacking.

"Jack," Sandor said as if he could read my mind, "it is not an easy path, and you are learning. Don't be too hard on yourself." He paused briefly. "Why don't we move on?"

"Okay." I was ready to change subjects. "Where to?"

"Let's look at someone else who was influenced by going to Seattle. Elton. Didn't he write you a letter about a trip to Whistler, British Columbia he took?"

"Yes, he did," I said, smiling. "That was a great letter."

"Focus on that and tell me what it said."

"With pleasure."

Dear Jack, MJ, and Sarah   *19 December 1989*

Greetings and Happy Holidays!!

This year I've been dreaming a dream. A grand dream. My grand dream. You have all heard me mention it at one time or another the last ten years, and you probably attributed it to my Irish heritage and gave it no more thought. I know I often have pushed it out of my mind so I could get on with the "serious" business of making a living. But this year it kept coming back, haunting my mind, my consciousness, and yes, even my dreams. And allow me right now to thank the person who most prodded those dreams: Sarah.

I have been very inspired by Sarah and her success with the Clinic. Not the monetary success; I'm sure she is still in debt from all the expenses of opening a healing center. No, I have been inspired by her success in life. She had her own grand dream, her own quest to find her true purpose in life. And she found it: To help and heal people, both in body and spirit. Then she did something about it. Now she is living her grand dream and fulfilling her grand purpose in life.

That's what I want.

So I took the steps to begin living my dream, not just dreaming it. I heard once that all you have to do to live your dreams is to wake up. Well, finally, I am awake. I've started on my dream. So have you guessed what it is yet? Well, I'll not drag out the suspense.

I want to start a brewery. A microbrewery. To brew real Irish ale, right here in America. It is what I have always wanted to do, but I have been afraid to take that leap —to risk money, security, and expose myself to the chance of failure. And after Maire and I were married, I became even more conservative. I told myself that I had responsibilities to fulfill, that I couldn't risk what we had for some old dream I had.

Along with the prodding from Sarah's success, two people changed my mind. One was Maire, and the other was Ingrid. Maire encouraged me to follow my bliss, that the passion and commitment I had for my dream made me vibrant, alive, and a man she wanted to be around, money or no. She wanted to join me in my quest, and was willing to do whatever it took to make it a reality.

I realized, and not for the first time, how lucky I was to have Maire as my partner, and how often I underestimated her. I proposed a trip up to Whistler Resort in British Columbia for us to ponder our future and for me to really come to grips with my bliss, my grand purpose in life. I wanted to make a good decision and be sure that I found my true path.

When I thought of going on such a quest, Whistler was my first choice. I thought the beauty and special character of Whistler would open me up to the universe and my own inner self to help me find my purpose. You probably remember I took a ski trip up there back when we were all at The Gatehouse. The skiing was brilliant, the village loads of fun, and the scenery spectacular in any direction you looked. Maire and I were going in October, so it wouldn't be ski season yet, but the scenery and the people would still be great, and we would be able to hike a bit at that time of year. It was at Whistler that I met Ingrid. Remember, I said earlier that two people changed my mind— Maire and Ingrid. Let me tell you the story of meeting Ingrid.

Maire and I had planned to fly to Vancouver, B.C., and then take B.C. Rail up to Whistler. The train ride was supposed to be awe-inspiring, climbing in elevation into the Canadian Cascades, passing over and by waterfalls and rapids, snowy peaks looming up around every bend. But at the last minute, Maire got an emergency call from work. She would have to delay her departure for two days to take care of the problem. Since we had pre-paid for five nights—and there was no way to change the days of our reservation—we decided that I should go up as originally planned and use the first two days to think about what I really wanted, write down all the pertinent facts, and to have some quiet, alone time to get in touch with my feelings and intuition. So off I went, excited like a schoolboy to finally begin to touch my dream.

The train ride was indeed stunning. I can't even describe its majesty. And they served a free breakfast on the train! When I reached Whistler it was still only mid-morning, and since check-in was not until 3:00 p.m. I decided to drop my bags at the lodging desk and cruise around town. It was chilly out at that time of morning and soon I began looking for a cafe to have some tea and perhaps a scone.

That was when I saw the sign for Ingrid's Cafe. It was a small place, really small, probably smaller than your office Jack, and empty at that time of the morning. It had three narrow "low" tables, and three equally narrow "high" tables that were built right into the wall and equipped with tall stools so you could reach your food. Ingrid was bent low working behind the counter, which had a deli display on one side with organic salads; a series of vegetarian style burgers such as potato, broccoli and cheese; bean and basmati rice, and fantastic falafel; along with traditional bavarian fare like bratwurst, schnitzel, and home-cooked sauerkraut. The other side of the L-shaped counter had a bakery display. It featured German marble cake, cinnamon raisin bread, low-sugar muffins, and strudel. Just then Ingrid lifted her head and caught me staring at her goods. She was a sultry blond with a voice like Marlene Dietrich, and a body to match.

"You like the looks of my strudel?" she asked. "It comes hot or cold...I like it hot."

I blushed and swallowed hard and tried to take my eyes off her proud bosoms, but I couldn't. She walked out from behind the counter, threw her leg up on a chair and started adjusting her black fishnet stockings. Her legs were as long and supple as her breasts were firm and taut. She turned and leaned back on the table and shot me a look that would steam broccoli.

"You want to try the strudel this morning? It's on the house..."

I felt my feet move on their own until I was over her reclining figure, her fishnets on either side of me. Our eyes met, then our hands, then our lips, and as the clothes fell off, the heavens opened and I felt truth as we...

Do I have your attention now? Do you think I have a future writing those books of love, lust, and power that are so popular these days? Okay, towel off and let's get back to business here.

First, one more thing about the strudel. Ingrid has a sign that says it is the best strudel in the village, but her vision is far too short. If there is better strudel in British Columbia or even Canada, I would be surprised. It's incredible.

Ingrid is a tall, thin woman of about 50 who speaks with a slight German accent, and moves about the cafe with a never-ending supply of energy. And the cafe is full of that good energy. Ingrid epitomizes spirit in the workplace. Her spirit is everywhere, and her love for people shows in all that she does. She greets her customers as they arrive, and thanks them as they depart. She asks how they are doing and answers questions with thoughtful responses and a continuing dialogue. All the while she is moving efficiently behind the counter, not rushed, but never slow, always apologizing for any delay, however slight. Her sense of humor is fine, dry and understated, with never a hint of a change in her voice or expression.

Besides enjoying her humor and her manner, I liked watching her care about her customers. A couple comes in at 11:30 and asks if she is still serving breakfast. The sign says she is not, and in fact she has now set up her prep areas for lunch. But her answer gets at the heart of the policy. It is not an inflexible policy just because it is on a sign.

"If I am not busy, I'll do breakfast," she says. " So, you just woke up, huh? What would you like?"

Told they would like the ham, egg, and croissant sandwich, she grimaces.

"I am out of croissants. I only use fresh baked croissants each day, so I make only what I think I will use. I'm sorry. But I will make you the same sandwich on a fresh bun for less money. Would that be acceptable?"

A principle strikes me here as I watch. Never compromise quality, but always have alternatives. And then as I think about her freshness policy, and look at her offerings of organic foods and vegetarian dishes, another principle strikes me. Do the very best you can for your customers, and do whatever you can to ensure their health, happiness, and enjoyment of life.

All this spirit and love and caring doesn't mean Ingrid isn't also a businesswoman. She knows that she can't help customers or her employees if she is out of business. When a family with a stroller comes in, she tells them they must sit in the corner or outside so the stroller is not in the way of everyone else in her small shop. When I linger too long in the warm atmosphere taking notes and writing letters, she throws me out to make way for new business. She's very polite, but firm. I move outside and, despite the 40-degree temperature, continue writing at her outside tables. 30 minutes later she is standing by my table, apologizing again and explaining why she had to ask me to leave.

"If people look in and see the tables full, most will leave and I will lose their business."

I already know this, of course; it is obvious with such a small place that she must turn the tables quickly. But the honesty and caring touch me and I realize a few truths.

We like people to care about us. All people. No matter how gruff we seem. And when they do, our spirit rises. A surge of energy courses through us.

We like the truth. More than a happy face and words, and way more than a down face and words. We like to hear truth from the heart. And the whole truth. Not slanted to make their side seem a bit more passable, or sugarcoated for us to swallow. When Ingrid explains why she had to ask me to leave, she says, "if people look in and see the tables full, most will leave." She could have said, "they will leave," or "they'll all leave," but she doesn't. Even though it would make her point stronger and her job of throwing me out less difficult, she knows it is not true. Some may get food to go; some may wait for a table to open; some may ask to sit with me. I know this, and when I hear her say it, I like it. It tells me she is fair. When she tells me the whole truth, I feel better, cared for, and trusting.

When that trust builds in the workplace, it changes the ethos (Jack, that is a fancy word for atmosphere. Use it at your next meeting of big shots and impress the heck out of them). We all feel it, and if truly bad news is brought forward, we trust that we are getting all the information, and that we are part of the process. We are in the minds and hearts of those making tough decisions. And, in fact, maybe we will be brought in on the decision-making process.

Our initial reaction to news, then, changes. We are not suspicious of the good and angry at the bad. We are free to rejoice in the good and be sad about the bad. But maybe also we can help fix the bad.

As I sat at Ingrid's writing this, I had an epiphany. I wanted to be in this kind of environment. I had been searching for it, longing for it, and I now realized that a big part of my purpose is to have my own brewery so I could create this type of environment myself. I could contribute to the world this way through my own love and caring for my customers and employees. I really wanted to make that happen. And after watching Ingrid that morning, I felt a special joy in my heart. For I knew that not only was the environment and spirit what I wanted, but the food and beverage business really was my love. And I knew I would be good at it.

I thanked Ingrid, left a big tip and went out to telephone Maire. I couldn't wait for her to arrive and to share my experience and my discovery. I just knew that Maire and I would be in sync on this.

I was raring to go. And two months later, I still am. Maire and I are researching our options. We are trying to decide if we should buy an existing brewery in the Phoenix area or build one, how to finance whichever one we choose, and so on. There is a lot of work ahead of us to get going, but overall, things are grand. And I already know what I shall call my first beer. Full Spirit Ale. Others may think that the spirit refers to liquor, which, of course, is sometimes called spirits. But you'll all know better. It is the spirit I hope to bring to my customers, employees, suppliers, community, family, and myself.

Take care, all of you. Bless you Sarah for your inspiration, and all of you start practicing your Irish jig for the grand opening!!!

Love,

Elton

"Your friends write good letters, Jack," Sandor said.

"Yes, they do." I sighed. "And it seems like they are all teaching..."

"Hang on, Jack," Sandor interupted. "Let's go a little further with your story before we probe any deeper into your actions and reactions."

"That's all right by me," I responded. "Those probes are starting to remind me of my annual trips to the doctor. Now that guy knows how to probe, and it ain't pleasant."

Sandor cleared his throat.

"Hey, you're trying not to laugh, aren't you? What, you don't think this is the proper time and place for proctology humor? Let me tell you, all guys know that there is no bad time for a good proctology joke. Excepting, of course, the first time you meet your in-laws and the yearly 'state of the company' address to the Board of Directors." Now I could hear him tittering. "I hear you there; just let it out like any good disembodied spirit would."

"I am not touching any of that, Jack," he managed to get out. "Let's move on. And don't call me a disembodied spirit. For all you know I am your own subconscious trying to get into that thick conscious head of yours."

"Yeah, right," I said flippantly while trying to think of a good comeback. But I couldn't. For all I knew it could have been my subconscious. I didn't have a clue. In the meantime, Sandor had resumed speaking.

"We can stay with Elton, though. Didn't he call you about nine months after his letter to talk about his business plan?"

"Yes, he did."

"And was that all you talked about?"

"No." I knew where he was going. "We talked about my dream."

"Excellent," he said. "A good subconscious loves to hear about dreams."

"You are not my subconscious," I said. "If I didn't know any better, I'd say you were getting cocky."

"Maybe you don't know any better."

"All right, enough. I don't think I'm in any condition to handle a disembodied, subconscious, gremlin of a smart-ass."

"As you wish," he said and I could hear the lightness in his tone.

"You're enjoying this, aren't you?"

"Yes, I am. Very much." His reply was so genuine it caught me by surprise.

I cleared my throat and fought my emotions. Funny how a little caring could touch you so fast.

"Go on, Jack," he said gently. "Tell your story."

thirteen

The phone rang early, before 8:00 a.m. one Sunday. Normally, I would have hopped out of the hammock and jogged in the house to get it. But normally by that time I would have been up for almost two hours. On this day, however, the shrill ring broke me out of a deep sleep. My inner alarm clock had not gone off, so I guess I must have needed the rest. Or perhaps I just needed to hear the message that was coming through in my dream.

I was following Sarah as she wound her way through a maze of corridors. I could not quite catch up to her, sometimes getting so near that I could smell the sweet fragrance of her hair as it flashed behind her; other times falling so far back that my breath would stop, escaping only in staccato stutters as I feared she had left me behind for good. She seemed to know the way, and glided through the turns and over the obstacles with very little effort, while I felt lost and out of control. Suddenly we came to a spacious field, beautiful with the colors of spring. A large path opened directly in front of me. My feet felt a burst of energy, and my body leaned forward. Sarah smiled and pointed me towards it, then turned and flew down a different path.

I stopped short. I wanted to follow her, but the pull of the path in front of me was strong. As she disappeared down her passageway, I stood frozen, unable to make any decision at all. I couldn't bear to let Sarah go, but the path in front of me was so alluring. For the first time in the dream, I felt like I could move effortlessly, like I wasn't just pushing on through the quagmire, but rather being pulled, as if someone or something on the other end wanted me. As I stood staring, suddenly a bell rang.

I jerked my head around; it was coming from another direction entirely. I could see a path there also, but it seemed to slant sharply upwards. The bell rang again and I turned and moved, reaching as I did...

Then I awoke, sprawled on the bed, one hand stretched towards the telephone.

"Hello," I mumbled trying to pull myself upright in bed.

"Jackie boy, is that you? You sound half asleep."

"It's me, Elton," I assured him, "and I am half asleep."

"You're always awake at this time of the morning. You're not sleeping one off, are you?" he kidded.

"No, no, I'm not sleeping one off. I've just been innocently dreaming." I hoped he'd take the bait. He did.

"What dreams? Tell me and then we can try to figure them out."

Elton had always been fascinated with dreams. He'd taken a seminar in Jungian analysis of dreams at school and had followed up with more research of his own. He would always urge Sarah, MJ, and me to tell him our dreams on Sunday mornings as we relaxed around the kitchen table or the hammock; then he would pop out some interpretations, or maybe grab one of his dream books and study it intently before coming out with his pronouncement. My head was still buzzing with my dream, and I definitely wanted some help figuring it out.

I filled Elton in on the dream, changing only the part about Sarah. I hadn't confessed my love of Sarah to anyone, and didn't want to start on a long distance call. I told him I was chasing an extraordinary woman—"I could feel it," I said—but that I couldn't make out her face.

"Well," he said when I finished the story, "here's what I think. The path that opened up to you, the one you were drawn to, the one where your feet and body felt free and eager to go, was your path. *Your* path, Jack. The Jack Path. The reason your physical being felt so in tune with it was because your spiritual being was in tune. If that is in tune it affects your physical being profoundly. You felt like, finally, this was your place to go. And you were certain. Weren't you?"

"Yes," I began, "but as certain as I was, I did not want to pass up..."

"I know, I know," he cut in, "you did not want to pass up the woman."

Not just any woman, I thought, but *the* woman—Sarah.

"I think this is a quite natural response, to not want to leave your dream woman. But you could see she was flying down her own path. Clearly she was meant to be a model to you, just as she went down her path, so must you go down yours. That is why it is there. And anything other than your path would be less than optimal."

"But what about the woman? I still don't want to lose her. Does my path naturally exclude the perfect woman? Am I doomed from the start to one or the other?" I took a deep breath and tried to calm myself. Even though this was just a dream and Elton was not Jung, I did not want to hear the "wrong" answer.

"No, I do not believe you are doomed to one or the other. What we don't know is what is *down your path*. It could be that your path and the mystery woman's path cross some time down the road. You'll never know, though, as long as you are afraid to travel your path."

This made instant sense to me. It didn't have to be one or the other; it could be both. I felt better already.

"You see the danger," Elton warned, "don't you? Only by following your path, as lonely and scary as that may look, can you hope to find the significant others—be they lovers, mentors or friends—with whom you were meant to share your life. You can't find them following someone else on their path."

"Elton, you're a genius. Gotta go now, though, and get back to sleep so I can start that dream over and find out what is down my path."

Elton laughed. "Glad to be of service. But before you sleep the day away, I have a question. Would you mind helping me on my business plan for the brewery?"

"Sure, I'll do whatever I can. What sort of help are you looking for?"

"Well, you remember the small brewery near here that we are trying to buy?"

"Of course," I said. "You thought it would be the perfect size to start with, and it had plenty of room for expansion later."

"Right. And everything about it still looks great."

"Is there a problem in the negotiations?" I inquired. "Are they asking too high a price?"

"No, the price is fair and the terms are fair. Our problem is finding more money, either through additional loans or a few investment partners."

"Are you seriously thinking about partners?" I asked. "Isn't one of your main goals being able to run the business the way you want to run it? Partners may want to impose their own will."

"Exactly why I am calling you, Jack. First off, any partners would be minority ones. But you are right in that even minority ones can cause problems if they want something different than the vision I am trying to create. So, I need to have partners who believe in running the business as I do. And to ensure that potential investors really understand where I'm coming from, I knew I would have to modify my business plan. I have been working on it for months, and have used it at various financing meetings already, but I haven't been satisfied. It sounded so stuffy, structured and lifeless. Figures and numbers and projections and on and on. I know you need those things in a business plan, but there was no heart, no soul, no spirit. No way for anyone to really know what I believed in, how much I believed it, or how I planned to run the business.

"As I attempt to acquire the rest of the financing and begin to build a 'brewery team,' I want that aspect of the business—the most important aspect—to show through. Even in a stuffy business plan. So I've taken another crack at it, and I would be most appreciative if you would review it and give me your comments."

"Absolutely, Elton," I replied. "But be careful with the touchy-feely stuff. You can turn a lot of investors off that way."

There was silence on the line.

"Elton, you there?"

"Yes, Jack. Just thinking. Your point is well taken, and certainly I need to have solid business data in my plan to show any investor that I know how to run it like a business. But, you know, I don't think I want the type of investor who is turned off by discussions about the heart and spirit of a business. I mean, if they think the financials make up the business, instead of being a by-product of how you run the business, then we are going to clash. And that will take a lot of the joy out of the day-to-day operations."

"I understand your point," I responded. "Just be careful about the mix. I think you need a good balance there or people will see you as a bleeding heart liberal with high ideals about people and love and togetherness, but no idea about how to run a business."

"Yes, you're right about the balance. Take a look at the whole plan when you get it, and let me know if I have missed the mark."

"No problem," I said. "You ought to send it to some others as well, and get several opinions."

"I'm doing that. I have about a half-dozen business executives and entrepreneurs who have agreed to look at it, and with you, MJ, and Sarah I should have a good mix of insight. Thanks for helping, Jack."

"My pleasure. Send it on and I'll get right to it. And thanks for your help with dream analysis. Now if I could only get back to the beautiful fields with my dream woman..."

"I shan't keep you any longer. Pleasant dreams, my boy."

"Thanks. Bye, Elton."

Of course, I couldn't go back to sleep that morning, and when I did that night I didn't wind up in the fields debating my path and yearning after Sarah. But a few days later Elton's business plan did show up.

FULL SPIRIT BREWERY BUSINESS PLAN

Table of Contents

Executive Summary

The goal of the Full Spirit Brewery is to brew the best lagers and ales in America. My years of experience in brewing and the secret recipes I brought from my homeland in Ireland will distinguish Full Spirit from other breweries. Our initial product line will feature Full Spirit Ale, a full-bodied ale reminiscent of Ireland's best ales; Limerick Lager, a crisp, light, refreshing lager to enjoy on a hot day; and Rosewood Stout, a thick, rich beer that is an experience in itself.

The Full Spirit Brewery's vision will be based on caring for employees, for the community and the environment. In turn, I believe, this will lead to employees who care, a community that cares, and a wonderful environment that all can enjoy. And when you have employees who care, the customers will feel it, they will like it and they'll care about which brand of ale they pick up and which one they recommend to their friends. This translates into captured customers, a strong brand, and—with good execution—profits.

Also, the community will begin to care and treat our business as a community partner. We will see the benefits of that caring in favorable community-based decisions on such issues as taxes, roads and water, as well as building a potential workforce for the future.

I realize this is not the typical start to a business plan. You may be wondering, are these just the words of a "do-gooder" on a mission? Or the insightful, far-reaching business strategies of a profit-making machine?

How about both? I want to do the right thing, and taking care of our employees, our customers, the community, and the environment is the right thing. But here's the business secret of the coming 21st century: Doing that *means* big profits. It is this combination that will take businesses into the next millennium, and make them successful. Business has to realize that people— and that means all of us—want to feel good about where we work, about what we buy, and about our contribution, whether that's developing new vaccines to save lives, or making ale. We want to do it right, and we want it to be the best. We want to feel pride in what we do.

We all want to be a part of making something that contributes to the greater good. Maybe it's beer, or gaskets, or helping people pick out the right paints and glazes, but underneath that rather "mundane job" is a fire. If you can tie that feeling of being the best at beer, or gaskets, or glazes, with specific policies and plans that demonstrate that *your* company will be involved—and allow you to be involved—in helping the world, the fire will ignite.

And that fire flames profits.

I believe that customers want to contribute to the greater good. And increasingly, they will frequent establishments and buy products from companies that reflect their values. They will ask themselves the question:

"Can I feel good about purchasing from this company?"

And even though it's just a six-pack of ale, if they know a few cents goes to help out, *visibly* help out; if they know the employees who make the ale volunteer and help the community, sometimes even on company time, that helps.

There is a business term for that called "good will." Investors pay millions for a brand with it.

We shall create it by the barrelful at Full Spirit Brewery.

And if our customers *want* to do business with Full Spirit; and our employees *want* to work at Full Spirit; and our suppliers *prefer* doing business with us, then that means profits. Big profits. And if a strong, vibrant community is in place, then we will be better able to attract and retain top talent. If the community *wants* us there, then decisions from the community that affect our business have a much better chance to be favorable.

Understand this clearly, though. I know a successful business needs good business practices, accounting structures, and operating policies. Because we care about employees, customers, suppliers, the environment, and the community doesn't mean that we will neglect being good business people. Poor business practices can drive a company out of business no matter what else they do. And you can't help your employees, community and the environment—and delight your customers—if you have an "out of business" sign on your door.

Management Plan

Business Philosophy

1) Let values and people guide the company in its quest for long-term profits.

2) Lead with the heart.

3) Let employees own a piece of the company. Not just physical ownership with shares of stock, but psychological ownership also, with shared values, shared vision, and employee involvement in all aspects of the business.

Employee Philosophy

1) Employees make our products and touch our customers. Nothing could be more important.

2) Trust between employees and their company leaders is a must. They must feel listened to, appreciated, and that they are getting their fair share of the rewards and company value. If they don't, distrust builds and everything the company leaders plan, propose, or do is undermined.

3) When employees relate to their company, and its values, goals, and culture, then they will pour their hearts into the company.

4) Their passion and devotion will be our competitive advantage. When they are engaged and fully present every day, we will out-produce and out-perform the competition.

5) Employees contribute more than they know—to their company, their family, their community, and to the world. They should do so consciously.

6) You can't treat employees as a cost to be contained.

Customer Philosophy

1) Always treat customers like family.

You mean forget their birthdays and yell at them during the holidays?

2) No, I mean cherish them. Customers are your lifeblood.

3) Help customers learn about your product. Teach them about ales. What's in them, how you make them, why they are better than the average beer.

Shareholder Philosophy

1) Shareholders are very important, and we will work hard for our shareholders; but if I think of them first I will sub-optimize the whole. Happy shareholders

are a by-product of happy other things—most notably employees and customers.

2) The Paradox—by not focusing on shareholders first, I will make them very happy and very wealthy.

3) The Shift—move from thinking just about share-holders and think instead about *stakeholders;* that is, all those with a stake in the company—employees, suppliers, the community and the shareholders.

Supplier Philosophy

Suppliers are partners in our business. Without them, we won't go very far. We will choose suppliers not only for their quality and prices, but also for their values and culture. We will cultivate strong, trusting relationships with our suppliers that will enable us to prosper in the good times, and join forces to weather the bad times.

Marketing Philosophy

Our great product, strong spirit, and intense enthusiasm will attract customers through word of mouth, our community involvement, and our retail outlet at the brewery. Brand recognition is important, and as the customers try to distinguish one from the other, our commitment to people, the community, and the environment will help us stand out. We'll start small and build a base of loyal, dedicated, informed customers who will be our best salespeople. And our base will be very dedicated, because not only will the product and our spirit attract them, but also many of them will share our values of contributing to the greater good. When they make that shift, their loyalty will grow and they won't leave Full Spirit for the sexy, new beer on the block or a big sale by one of the beer companies whose forte is marketing.

When we sell our ales, we will make it a special experience, an experience that will stand out in our customers' minds. We will teach our customers about our ales, the special waters we use, the grains, how the malt makes a beer sweeter and the hops give it that bite. We will train our people—all of them—in what we do, how we do it, and what we believe in. They will be our link to the world and will communicate our passion to the customers.

As a microbrewery, we will be on the cutting edge of a growing trend. Micro brews are becoming popular across North America. Successful microbrews such as Red Hook and Pyramid have used the European tradition of brewing local beers and winning substantial market shares in the local area. Building excellent distribution systems then allows for expansion into other markets. Full Spirit will follow this successful formula of building a strong regional following and then expanding. Our superior brewing process will separate us from the pack of watered-down, mass-marketed beers, and our Irish feel and flavor will differentiate us from other microbrews. Detailed marketing and competition data is in the marketing annex of this plan.

Philosophy on Fun

We will emphasize it! We want our employees and customers to have fun, and we want fun to be associated with Full Spirit Brewery. We want humor and playfulness to be a part of our experience.

Community Service and Giving Philosophy

Working with and contributing to the community is critical to the success of our business for several reasons.

1) It will raise our profile in every community we work with, and that is like free advertising. And "good will" grows rapidly in that environment.

2) Our employees will be proud to work in a company that cares about something more than money. Their spirit and motivation will rise, and so will our productivity.

3) And finally, it's the right thing to do. Especially for me. I need to be involved. I can't start a company and not participate in the greater good of the community and world. We are all here for a reason, and one way or another that reason revolves around helping people and the planet. This is my chance to contribute on a grander scale, and I won't let it slip by—especially when I know that it will improve our bottom line enormously.

CEO Philosophy: My Role

1) In the beginning, everything, including sweeping the floors if need be.

2) Being a leader and a visionary.

3) Caring about all stakeholders. Improving their value stake every day.

4) Taking responsibility to never sacrifice quality for short-term benefits. We will build our reputation and authenticity around the quality of our ales. Shortcutting our brewing process or products to save a few dollars will reduce us to just another beer maker, and that will kill us in the end. Our product is quality. It is the spiritual flavor of the beer we make.

Bottom line

1) When you treat and manage your employees very well and give them top-of-the-line pay and benefits, you will reduce turnover, which, in turn, will reduce recruiting, and training—both high expense items.

2) Experienced employees are more productive, and those dealing with customers can develop relationships that will last. Customers respond to that kind of stability, and enjoy the human connection.

3) Happy employees come to work on time, miss fewer days and don't strike.

4) Healthy, safe employees stay on the job and add to the productivity.

5) The "soft" stuff is really the hard stuff. That's why I'm spending so much time on that aspect of the business. It's hard to get people engaged and keep them that way. It's hard to build trust and retain it. It's hard to grow the kind of loyalty that has people going the extra mile—or perhaps two or three—without even being asked. It's hard to build the kind of company where people want to work —and want their friends and family to work there, too. It's hard, but we will do it at Full Spirit, much to the benefit of the bottom-line.

Final Thoughts

National statistics and corporate surveys are becoming very clear. The cost to business of problems such as employee turnover, absenteeism, and poor morale is huge and growing. Billions of dollars annually go to recruitment and training of new employees to replace ones we have lost. Not to mention the loss of productivity as new hires come up to speed. Lost workdays due to accidents, absenteeism, and chronic lateness are costly signs of a workforce with low morale and no common vision that connects the employee and the company. Our policies and intentions at Full Spirit Brewery are designed to reduce those costs to an absolute minimum, and increase profits through high productivity, loyal customers, and contagious enthusiasm. I know we can do it. Will you join us in our quest?

Thank you for taking the time to read the Executive Summary and Management Plan. If you have any questions on anything you have read here, please don't hesitate to contact me. Now, for your further reading pleasure, the margin model by product line is presented, then our P&L projections, then...

"Sandor, you there? What do you think of Elton's business plan?" I waited for a reply. "Sandor?" Nothing. Just when I was going to give up his voice broke through.

"Yes, Jack, I am here. I liked Elton's plan. What did you think of it when you first read it?"

"Impressive. Well-written, excellent numbers and projections, and the executive summary was unlike any I had read before. In my position then as an executive VP, his thoughts on running a business intrigued me." I anticipated his next question and kept going. "But this was an incredible time at Dynamics. Our expansion plans into the Pacific Rim were going full bore. I was traveling frequently—practically living in the Far East—focused totally, and really enjoying the different cultures and the challenges. Unfortunately, I wasn't around much to follow up with Sarah other than some letters, or to consider Elton's management philosophy."

"But there's a difference this time from the previous times you missed or ignored a message, isn't there, Jack? Didn't you return to Elton's Plan and reconsider it?"

"I did," I said and felt a strange burst of pride and happiness. It felt good to be saying that I had actually followed up on something, albeit eighteen months later. That's when I received another letter from Elton reporting on the success of his new brewery.

By then my life was very different...

<small>chapter</small> fourteen

"Jack, let's enjoy this," Sandor said. "I want you to tell the story of the Iditirod racers and your review of Elton's business plan. But start the morning you called MJ, and include how you felt as you headed to your office."

"Yes sir," I said happily. This was a story I loved to tell.

"And be clear about your thought patterns, your concerns, and your focus on doing the right thing."

"Okay, I'll try."

I got up even earlier than usual that morning, and headed down to the office. It was a Saturday, so I knew I would have some time to myself to catch up on paperwork, and also to just think and reflect. There hadn't been much time for that lately.

As I walked towards my office, my anticipation grew. Yes, there it was above my name. *Chief Executive Officer.*

I smiled. It had been eight months since I had been named CEO, and so far I had not tired of looking at my title. I had made it. CEO! After all those years of dreaming, the hard work had paid off. But lately another thought had been nagging at me: Did I know what I was doing?

In all my other jobs I had been given a clear set of objectives—and I was a bulldog when it came to reaching objectives. But those had been mostly tactical, dealing with programs and projects, proposals and products. My CEO job description wasn't so clear. I had been chosen over several older and more experienced VPs because the Board of Directors wanted some new blood at the top. Our retiring CEO—who was becoming

Chairman of the Board—had been the deciding factor in my getting the job. I had been told in private by one of the Board members that our CEO had made a very passionate speech to the Board. He said that things were definitely changing, but no one really knew how, or how much. Dynamics needed to be ahead of that change. But it was going to take an enormous amount of energy and someone who would never be satisfied until the conundrum was figured out. That, our CEO had said, was a description of me. He didn't think I had the answers any more than any other VP, but he felt my absolute dedication to success and my all-consuming focus on the job would give me the best chance to figure out the changing world, and position Dynamics ahead of the tidal wave.

The day they gave me the job, they told me that I needed to lead the company in this new and changing world. They also gave me a mandate to grow and diversify the company, and to make it more profitable. They included some targets associated with that, but they were broad targets such as achieving a certain percentage of growth, or raising the stock price to a certain level.

The big question was: How did a CEO make all that happen? What was my role in all this, how did I *lead*—and I had heard that word a lot—the company to the next level of excellence? After eight months of getting my feet wet, I still didn't have the answer to that question.

The day before, I had received a letter from Elton. The financial numbers for the first year of operations of Full Spirit Brewery were in. They had far exceeded expectations, actually making a profit in the first year. That letter had started me thinking, and I had rummaged around until I found my copy of Elton's business plan. I had helped with some of the numbers, financial projections and so forth, but the part I wanted to review had to do with Elton's ideas about valuing and connecting employees, customers, suppliers, and the community. I had it with me that morning, and I sipped some coffee as I browsed through it.

- The Paradox—By not focusing on shareholders first, I will make them very happy and very wealthy.

- The Shift—move from thinking just about share-holders and think instead about stakeholders; that is, all those with a stake in the company—employees, suppliers, the community and the shareholders.

- Our employees will be proud to work in a company that cares about something more than money. Their spirit and motivation will rise, and so will our productivity.

- Let values and people drive the company towards long-term profits.

This was Elton thinking like a CEO for his company. It was clear what he was valuing, and where he thought his attention should be focused. I knew I wasn't focused on these same areas, that I wasn't thinking like Elton was as a CEO. But should I be? After all, I rationalized to myself, his is a much smaller company. How could I focus my time on that kind of stuff when I had possible mergers, labor negotiations, unfair trade practices, and any number of other worldwide issues to contend with?

Still, I was forced to admit, focusing on employees, customers, suppliers and the community did sound an awful lot like what a CEO should be doing. And I remembered my conversation with Vincent some years ago. He had been saying much the same thing. His emphasis over and over had been on the people of the company and my responsibility to them. Not what they had to do for me, even though they worked for me, but rather, what I had to do for them, my role in helping to make the considerable time they spent at work meaningful, and fostering an environment that valued them not only as employees, but also as people.

And both Elton and Vincent had been very clear that this was not just a philanthropic gesture. By valuing employees and setting up the right environment for them, their spirits would be engaged, creativity would emerge, turnover and absenteeism would plummet, customers would become engaged and loyal—and the company would make a pile of money. A win-win situation, in today's management lingo.

I needed to explore this further. And I knew a fun way to start. Call MJ. She was living in the Bay Area again, doing fabulously as minority owner of a Body Shop store. She had stayed on in England for three years working at several of the shops, then finally gotten homesick and returned. But she told The Body Shop executives that she wanted to be a part of a Body Shop in the San Francisco area, and they had helped broker a deal where a woman with money but no experience received 67% of the business; and MJ, with a little money and lots of know-how and experience, received 33%. MJ also had obligations to manage the shop, work long hours and, in general, pay for her piece with years of sweat equity. In the four years since the shop opened, they had doubled revenues every year and MJ was always quick to point out how the corporation contributed to their success by caring for the employees and the community and consistently delivering the message that integrity, ethics, and values mattered. I needed to hear more about how all that worked.

And I had the perfect incentive for MJ. I had booked speakers from the great Iditarod race in Alaska to give a motivational talk to our management team. I'm not sure what had made me book a bunch of "mushers." I had read an article in the Wall Street Journal and it had sounded interesting. But I was a little hesitant to schedule something where I couldn't do a clear ROI—return on investment—analysis. In the end, I followed my gut and set it up. If nothing else, it would give my managers some different ideas. And it was a perfect opening for my call to MJ. I knew she had a real admiration for those brave souls who raced with dog sleds 1,200 miles from Anchorage to Nome, and for the incredible dogs. She also was fond of pointing out that in the last several years more women than men had won the race.

It was still pretty early, but I figured MJ would be up getting ready for work, so I called. She answered rather sleepily.

"Hullo."

"MJ, is that you, or have I awakened a hibernating bear?"

"Jack, is that you?" she sputtered.

"No fair copying my question, MJ."

"What time is it, Jack?"

"It's wake-up time, time to get ready to go in to that incredible store of yours."

"I'm closing today, Jack. I don't go in until noon," she protested. "I could have slept for two more hours."

"Well, now that you're already up, I have a proposition for you."

"It better be good," she said and I could hear her moving in the bed, probably trying to sit up.

"It is," I assured her. "It would be worth getting up even earlier than this."

"Don't push your luck," she said. "I'm listening."

"All right. I would like to invite you to be my guest at a special multimedia presentation to be given by several participants in this year's Iditarod Race, and at the private reception following."

I heard her gasp. "Are you serious? Don't mess with me on this, Jack."

"I am serious. Scout's honor."

"Who are the speakers going to be?" she asked excitedly. "Is Susan Butcher one?" naming perhaps the most successful racer, man or woman, who ever shouted, "Mush."

"I'm not sure," I replied, "but there are going to be several champions there, so Susan would be a pretty good bet."

"Thank you, Jack, for thinking of me."

"No problem, and if you don't mind, I'd like to pick your brain about The Body Shop."

"Sure," she replied, "that's a subject I love to discuss."

"Great. The presentation is Wednesday at 2:00 p.m., reception to follow. Meet me at my office, which, of course, is now in the headquarters building."

"Oh, I can't wait to see the fancy digs."

"Feel free to give me any decorating advice when you get here. See you then."

"Bye, Jack. Thanks again for the invitation."

I hung up and leaned back. Let the education begin.

I was poring over some financial data when my secretary buzzed. "Your friend MJ is here."

"Thanks, Berta." Berta, short for Roberta, had been with me for the last eight years and we had climbed the ladder together. Without her, my life would be twice as hard and half as efficient. "Show her in, please."

MJ came in and stopped cold. "Wow, this is very nice. And big. I never got anywhere near the 'head shed' when I worked here. I didn't know it was quite this swanky."

"Yes, swanky city is our nickname for it. They call me Mr. Swank."

"Jack, you're making fun of me. Please stop or I'll be forced to pound you in front of your adoring staff."

I laughed. "Okay, come on in. Let me get you something to drink." I got us a couple of Calistoga mineral waters from the small refrigerator that was built into the combination bookshelf, display case and wet bar.

"This is very impressive, Jack. And not just the office, but the fact that you made it here. You worked hard and kept your eyes on your goal, and you made it happen. You should be very proud of yourself."

I blushed and stuttered. I was not very good at receiving compliments, especially from people I really cared about. MJ laughed and I looked over quickly to see if she was laughing at me. But her head was tilted back and she had a faraway look in her eye.

"Remember when we met? Who would have thought that a guy who cut his first ever company function..."

"The orientation," I interjected.

"...would become the CEO twenty years later. Only 45 years old. The youngest CEO in company history, if I remember the newspaper right."

"Well, now this youngest guy has to perform or he'll be the youngest CEO ever to be canned."

"It looks like you are doing a good job so far to me, Jack. I follow your stock. That seems to be good. And the earnings reports I've seen are up significantly."

"Yes, so far, so good. But as CEO, I need to be looking out further, and I really need to focus my time on the right things. But I'm not convinced I know what those things are. That's why I wanted to talk to you. It seems your company has a little different philosophy than we do. And when I went over Elton's business plan a few days ago, I got some of that same flavor: Of focusing on people and relationships and values, and building the culture where people are engaged, creativity soars, and the intensity and commitment of the people drive ever increasing profits."

"When you say it like that," MJ said, "it sounds so obvious. Like, of course, you should be doing that."

"I know," I said. "That's my problem. When I shift my point of view, it sounds so damn obvious, yet that isn't how we have done it before here, nor do I see it with our competitors. And we have been pretty successful over the years." I paused and a sigh escaped.

"This not only feels like uncharted waters, it feels like very dangerous waters. If I break new ground and am unsuccessful, it seems like I will be in more danger than if I do the same old thing and it is unsuccessful. At least then I would have all the standard excuses of economic recessions, or inflation, or global monetary crises or whatever."

"Jack, it seems to me that the real job description of a CEO is to lead the company into the new uncharted waters of the future, and to see that future more clearly than anyone else. The glimpse you are getting of the future tells you that you need to focus on people more. And do some things differently. That scares you. And it should. But that's the risk you take when you sign on to be CEO. I think that is a key part of the job description: *To have the courage to do the right thing.*

"Even if it is bucking history, and even if you know you're going to get some flack from traditionalists and conservatives in the executive suites and on the Board."

She really made a lot of sense. "MJ, I don't mean this in a derogatory way at all, but you have really come a long way since our days here. You had no interest in business then, you were always more into..."

"People and relationships," she finished. "I know, and at that time, that kind of a focus got me nowhere in the company. That's why when I hooked up with The Body Shop I suddenly felt like I was home. What I was good at—people and relationships—was important and valued there. After a while, though, I realized that if I were to stay in this field, and get to my dream of owning a Body Shop, I would have to know more about the business aspects. So I have studied and read business books, and most of all, watched how The Body Shop handled all kinds of issues as they grew and expanded. And I asked a lot of questions." She took a sip of her mineral water.

"So you and I are coming at this from different sides, Jack, but it seems like we are both trying to achieve the right balance. A solid focus on business, but with a realization that the greatest leverage we have is our people." She started to reach for her water again, then suddenly jumped up in typical MJ fashion.

"Oh, I just thought of something else. As CEO, you need to see the future clearly and chart a course." She was starting to pace and her arms were moving as she tried to capture her thought. "On a broad level, you do it by seeing key issues or opportunities—like focusing on people, or new strategies, or possible mergers—and having the courage to do it. But, if you look on a technical and product level, the company still needs to see into the future and do breakthrough thinking. But the only ones who can see that future and create it are your employees—because, of course, you personally cannot sniff out each innovation and advancement in the hundreds or thousands of areas you need them in to remain at the top." She turned and studied me before continuing.

"That seems to validate your idea even more, Jack. To take care of the future as CEO, you have to spot the big roads and highways, but you also have to help set the environment and provide the tools and resources so the rest of your people can invent, create, integrate, and maintain the huge infrastructure that supports the company as it zooms over the highway." She sucked in some air, shook her head and frowned. "Did that analogy fall apart?"

"It was teetering," I said, grinning, "but I get the point. The future's on a couple levels, and even I, Jack the Dedicated, can't do 30,000 plus jobs by myself. So I had better focus on creating the atmosphere and environment that values people, provide them tools and methods so they can think, innovate, and produce more efficiently and effectively; and then make sure they are focused on the business so the end result is a more productive and profitable company. And while they take care of the innovative product and process level, I'll continue looking out over the horizon and steer for the long term." I glanced at the clock on the wall and jumped up.

"Whoa, we'd better get a move on or we'll be late." As we reached the door, I stopped and looked her in the eye. "Thanks, MJ. I really appreciate your help, and I value our friendship more than you probably will ever know."

Now it was her turn to blush, and she stepped forward and hugged me. I hugged her back tightly. I was surprised at how good it felt to be connected emotionally and physically to someone. Other than weekends with Elizabeth, now seven and amazing in every way, I'd had very little connection lately.

After the event was over and MJ had headed home, I returned to my office, leaned back in my chair and gazed out the window. Unlike that first office of mine where I only saw asphalt and parked cars, the view from the eighth floor showed the valley in all its beauty. At this time of night, lights flared from bridges and buildings, and jets starting their final approach to San Francisco Airport flickered in the distance. Watching this free show was a gift to myself after a long day, and it gave me something to look forward to as I plowed through the endless piles of items to read or sign or make a decision on.

It had been a special day with MJ and the Iditarod guests. The view outside my window was special too, but it wasn't what I saw that struck me. It was what I heard. Voices were rattling around in my head and the message was becoming harder to ignore. MJ, Elton, Vincent, Sarah, my first boss Ed, Elton's parents, my parents, Steve's thesis on Management by Moe, Father Antonio's picnic notes and cryptic fragments of advice, and on and on. Messages of people and values, of integrity and good will, of stakeholders, not shareholders.

And that day, messages from mushers. Messages that also struck home —even though a musher didn't have people to lead, just dogs. The final speaker was especially good. And her dogs! They looked amazing, even on videotape. They were gorgeous with thick coats that seemed to sparkle, they were so clean and bright. Their eyes shone with a fierce intensity, and their paws and nails were cleaned and clipped. She treated them with a special reverence, and the love was evident on both sides as she discussed them. I had asked her later about this special treatment and love, and she said the dogs were her lifeblood. Without them, she couldn't race at all. They were her most critical resource.

Sitting there, comfortable and relaxed, I could see something was out of whack. Our company slogan the last few years had been, "people are our number one asset." Just like her dogs, without our people we couldn't win the race, or even line up at the starting line. That seemed true, and our slogan indicated we knew it to be true.

So why didn't we treat our people with the same love and reverence with which she treated those dogs? I became defensive about my own question, and started listing the reasons in my head.

1) Her dogs were specially trained for one task a year.

2) Love and reverence weren't work qualities, these were for the home.

3) Dogs are natural suck-ups.

4) People aren't dogs. (That didn't hold much water. Aren't we supposed to treat them better than dogs?)

5) Manicures and pedicures for 30,000 could be prohibitively expensive.

As I looked at the arguments, none of them seemed very convincing except for the manicure/pedicure one. (Even then, I remembered reading that some companies were doing employee massage.) Why couldn't we treat our employees with the same love, care, and reverence a musher shared with her dogs?

I picked up the phone. Time to go to the next phase of my plan. The phone rang, then I heard the telltale click.

"Hello, this is Elton, of Full Spirit Brewery. I'd love to talk with you, so please leave your name and number and I'll get back to you right away. If this is an emergency..."

Well, this might have been an emergency for me, but I was pretty sure it wasn't for Elton. I waited for the beep.

"Hey, Elton, Jack here. When are you going to start working full days, mate? Heck, it's only 9:00 p.m.; the day's just getting started.

"Okay, before you beep again and cut me off, here's what I am thinking. I have been re-reading your business plan, as well as listening to some wise folks here at Dynamics, chatting with MJ, and even having a drink with an Iditarod musher. All are making the same points about people and environment and stakeholders and so on. Elton ol' friend, I need your help. Think you could spare some time to come out here? The sooner the better. You could see the environment for yourself, and we can stay up late watching Stooge re-runs and trying to figure out how the hell I can start making all this good stuff happen. And maybe you can explain the good stuff one more time so I get it. Let me know, big guy. Talk to you soon, bye."

The next day I was out with customers in the morning and when I returned Elton had left a message on my voice mail.

"Jack, I would love to help you in your quest to generate spirit and whole-heartedness at work. Those are hard to define subjects, and it's even harder to put a plan into place that will result in those attributes coming alive in your company. But there is one thing we all know, whether we are CEOs or mail room clerks: If our company has spirit, we leap ahead of the competition and amaze even ourselves. And if we don't, we are dying a slow—or not so slow—death. So it is time to at least start raising questions about spirit in the workplace—and about spirit in our lives.

"I have to go to the doctor this afternoon, but I will call you this weekend and we can start the discussion."

In fact, Elton did not call that weekend or the next, but left me a message at home the following week. He apologized for not responding as he had promised. He had been in and out of the doctors' offices lately, and had wanted to understand his medical situation before he called.

Now he understood, and he wanted to take a rain check on visiting me. You see, he said, he had to start some therapy. He had cancer.

fifteen

"Jack, I know this is hard," Sandor said, "but you must continue with your story. Tell me what happened then."

My world turned upside down. The thought of losing Elton paralyzed me. I had trouble eating, sleeping, functioning at all. Death had always been an abstraction to me. No one I knew had ever died unless they were at least eighty years old. I had just begun to think about the possibility of my parents reaching an age of risk; it was inconceivable that someone younger than me, and my best friend, would have a life-threatening illness. Elton, on the other hand, was handling it better.

"I'll beat it, Jack," he reassured me. "Lots of folks do these days, you know."

But when I talked to Sarah, she was not so optimistic.

"The cancer is in the pancreas, Jack. I'll know more after I see him, talk to his doctors, and review all the x-rays and imaging scans, but the odds can't be too high. The pancreas is vital, and a cancer there is very hard to treat."

Sarah flew down to Phoenix several times over the next six months. She reviewed all the data on Elton, consulted with his doctors, and designed a plan to supplement the more traditional treatments he had already started. There were diet changes, internal cleansings, homeopathic medicines, herbs, guided visualizations and more.

All the while Elton was optimistic, and in our frequent phone conversations his mood and energy began to sway me towards thinking a recovery was likely. My spirits rose and I began to function better, attacking my CEO role with more of my usual vigor. One Thursday, Berta stuck her head into my office. I was meeting with a few of my VPs.

"It's Elton," she said. I had given her instructions as soon as Elton got sick that anytime he called, interrupt me.

"Let's take a break," I said to the VPs and Berta escorted them out.

"Elton," I exclaimed.

"Hey, Jack, I won't keep you long, I know you must be busy, but I have a request."

"You name it, Elton," I said.

"How about popping down for a long weekend. Now, before you answer, let me give you some additional incentive. If you can get here by tomorrow afternoon, you'll cross paths with our favorite Doctor—Sarah. She'll be leaving tomorrow, but not until the evening."

I glanced at my schedule for tomorrow, but didn't look long. This was a no-brainer, even for a workaholic like me.

"I'll be there, Elton. You don't have to pick me up"—he always insisted, but it was almost thirty miles from his house to the airport and I knew he and Maire had better things to do—"give my best to Maire and tell Sarah I'll give her a ride to the airport tomorrow night." He didn't protest this time.

"That's grand, Jack. See you then."

I hung up and buzzed Berta.

"Can you reschedule my afternoon appointments and get me to Phoenix by about three o'clock tomorrow?"

"You betcha," she said. "You could use a little fun and relaxation."

It turned out that I could use—in fact really needed—what I experienced in Phoenix that weekend, and many to follow. But fun and relaxation are not good descriptions of what happens when you are forced to build your character and test your soul.

I flew to Phoenix the next afternoon, picked up a rental car and headed out to Elton's. Maire answered the door and hugged me tightly, her voice catching as she greeted me. She led me into the kitchen. I saw Sarah first carrying a pitcher of iced tea towards the table. Then I saw Elton, and I couldn't help but gasp. He was so thin—gaunt, really. He had a smile on his face as he pushed himself off his chair and came to me. I was frozen. I knew I should act like nothing was the matter, try to be encouraging about his appearance, but I couldn't speak. All I could think was that he was dying. Really dying. He hugged me and tried to put me at ease.

"Hello, Jack, so glad you could come. As you can see, that much-needed diet is working, and soon I'll be down to my fighting weight. I think I may get a crack at the Bantamweight title next year." He gave me a quick one-two on the arm. I feinted a punch back and tried to think of something witty to say. But my mind was still frozen. Sarah jumped in to save me this time.

"Hungry, Jack? Maire is fixing her famous fajitas for me so I don't have to eat those nasty peanuts on the plane back to Seattle."

I nodded, accepted a glass of iced tea and allowed Sarah to lead me out to the patio. Elton had installed a mister that sprayed a fine water mist in the air and made it comfortable outside (as long as you were in the shade). Elton was very talkative, chatting about the brewery, the great people there, new customers, local sports, the weather. This was the Elton I remembered from the phone calls, the optimistic one who *sounded* very healthy. His eyes sparkled and his hands were animated. Maybe he was getting better and the weight was just lagging behind. I slowly regained my bearings and joined in the conversation. Maire served the fajitas, then some ice cream, and it was time for Sarah to leave.

I loaded her bag into my rental car and headed for the airport. I had planned to do this so I could have some time alone with her. Now I needed the time alone for another reason. As I started down the road I turned to her, looking hard into her face, hoping for that miracle. She knew my questions before I asked.

"I don't think so, Jack," she said, "the cancer is so advanced that..."

Her eyes welled up and she stopped. I reached out and took her hand and we drove in silence for a while. I was blinking hard to keep my eyes in focus as the tears formed, and I was sniffling as my nose began to run. I didn't have any tissue in the rental car, and it wouldn't have mattered anyway because I needed a hand on the wheel as I tried to keep the car on the road. My other hand held Sarah's tightly, and neither of us would let go. We needed the human touch then, and as my eyes overflowed and ran fast down my cheeks I let the car drift to the side of the road. As one tire ran up the curb my grief overwhelmed me, and I began sobbing uncontrollably. Sarah's petite body was already trembling with the force of her sobs, and we turned and laid our heads on each other's shoulders and cried a puddle onto the vinyl seat of the rental car.

When I returned to Elton's he was on the patio under the sun umbrella, waiting for me in one of his new deck chairs. He had gotten them the week before and I asked what had prompted his purchase.

"I thought they'd be handy for my wake," he said.

"Oh, Elton, don't say that," I said. "I thought you were getting better. You've sounded so much better on the phone lately."

"I have been getting better, Jack—but not physically. Spiritually, I feel better than I ever have. This illness has forced me to look at life—and after-life—with a lot more focus and intensity. Also," he paused and waved his hands over the chairs, "I've had more time to shop for cool stuff, like these chairs. See how these are kind of like director's chairs, taller, with armrests and backs. They are very comfortable and I'm going to put your names on them so you'll have the honored seats during the wake. One for you, one for MJ, one for Sarah..."

I cut in, unsure of what to say, but wanting him to stop. "Elton...stop...you're not...going...to die."

"Yes, I am, Jack."

That hung in the air several seconds, then his eyes twinkled.

"But, so are you. I'm just first, as usual."

I laughed, boxed him playfully as we always had done, (but this time much more gently), and excused myself to go to the bathroom. I splashed cold water on my face and gazed in the mirror. I looked like hell; puffy face, red eyes, and my wrinkles looked like they'd been highlighted with an Etch-a-Sketch.

"Jack, this dying stuff sure is tough," I said to myself in the mirror. The image in the mirror nodded agreement and added: "But, this is real life, so you'd better get used to it." I buried my face in a towel to dry it and went back out. Elton seemed to know my bathroom visit included more than bladder relief.

"What's going on in your head, Jackman?" he asked.

I hesitated for a second, then figured "what the hell" and told him. I finished with the quotation about this being "real life so you'd better get used to it."

He stared hard at me, almost into me. "No, it's not," he finally said.

I was confused. "Not what?"

"Not real life. Remember the quote by Teilhard de Chardin that Father Antonio put in our picnic basket one time?"

I looked at him blankly so he continued. "'We are not human beings having a spiritual experience. We are spiritual beings having a human experience.' Do you believe that, Jack?"

"I don't know," I said truthfully.

"Well, I do," Elton said with conviction. "And I want you to help me prove it."

"Me," I squeaked. "How am I going to do that?"

"I don't know," he answered. "That's what you and I have to figure out in these last weeks."

A loving, warm and confident smile creased his face. He was calm, relaxed, peaceful and not at all afraid. I knew what I looked like, and it wasn't any of those. Maybe there was something to what Teilhard de Chardin had written. It was clear that I was dead-bolted into a human experience, but my dear friend Elton seemed to be more fully into a spiritual experience the closer he came to that "transition." Now I needed to help Elton, and I knew that wouldn't be easy.

We spent some quality time together in the best discussions we'd had in a long time, the way the most profound conversations sometimes come at the end of a party when you are saying goodbye. Mostly I learned and listened to a man I was proud to call my friend.

On Sunday I returned home, wondering how long it would be until I received the call that would bring me back. A call I dreaded, but knew was coming nonetheless. A continuing of my own rites of passage. First, the breakdown of my marriage, then reaching my pinnacle of success—CEO—and realizing that didn't make life perfect, and now facing the loss of my best friend. I wondered why he hadn't let me know how bad his condition had become; then I realized that he knew I didn't want to hear it. I wanted so badly for him to be all right, and the hope for me was easier than the truth. So he had waited to tell me in person. He was shepherding me through another tough time. What was I going to do without him?

Not long after, I received a call from Maire that Elton had returned to the hospital. I flew back down, and at Maire's request I went to the hospital to bring Elton back home for the final days.

I pushed the wheelchair down the hall of the oncology ward with Elton smiling and winking at the nurses, doctors, patients, service personnel and all the other friends he had made in his many visits there. They waved back, touched him on the arm, shouted encouragement and words of love. It was almost surreal, a scene from an adventure novel where the healed hero heads out amidst the cheers of his comrades; or a medical miracle story, where the patient is pushed out of the hospital after beating the incurable disease and inspiring all those around him.

But this wasn't a story of beating the odds to be physically well again. Elton was leaving not because he was cured, but because they couldn't do anything else for him. This wasn't a stroll down victory lane; yet, as I rolled him down that hall, it sure seemed like it. And then I realized what kind of story this was.

Elton had beaten the odds, all right. Not the physical odds— the spiritual ones. And all those in the hallway knew it. They could see it in his eyes, in his voice, in his sparkle and vibrancy. His spirit wasn't afraid of dying. He knew his sickness would not, could not, beat him.

As I walked behind Elton's wheelchair during his final departure from the hospital, my eyes welled up with tears, but this time not from sadness—it was pride at his dignity, and that I was his friend. I turned the wheelchair around at the end of the hall and Elton and I looked back down the narrow corridor. Everyone was still there. Elton lifted his hand in the air and clenched his fist. The cheering grew louder as the hallway group reacted like a Wrigley Field bleacher scene, fists pumping in the air and wide smiles showing. I saw and heard it all, but suddenly it dimmed, as if my ears had plugged while descending in a jet, then my mind cleared and focused sharply and I saw the obvious.

Elton was changing people's lives. He had been doing so for the last several months, and was doing so most dramatically right now, in the present. These people had looked to him and he had opened himself up, and inside they had seen spirit—not fear, or hatred, or a victim's mentality, but pure, loving spirit. That changes lives. I had heard people talk about spirit, but seeing and feeling it, I now understood what it meant. And having experienced how Elton lived his life in each moment and built his business with spirit in the workplace—I knew his message would live on. This is what true leadership looks like, I thought to myself.

I turned the wheelchair to the left and we headed for the elevator. I touched Elton's shoulders. "Thanks for letting me be here."

He just laid his thin hand on mine.

Maire waited in the front yard, ready to receive her beloved husband. It was clear that they shared a deep devotion. As I wheeled him around to the backyard ramp, the peaceful moment evaporated in an atmosphere of bustling activity. Workmen were there following Elton's list of improvements to be done prior to the wake. The biggest project was inspired by Sarah's clinic. The waterfall in Sarah's treatment room had appealed greatly to Elton, and he had arranged for a large waterfall to be built in the backyard that would pump his ale at the wake. The workmen had just finished hooking it up and were making some final adjustments. Elton loved it, as did I. Maire just rolled her eyes, shaking her head from side to side. We would all miss Elton's sense of humor.

Elton's family began to arrive over the next few days. He was weak, of course, and needed quite a bit of rest, but when he was up, he was clearly in charge. He knew what he wanted, and seemed to have the timetable all laid out.

"You can't plan dying like you plan a wedding," I protested once.

"Why not?" he asked in a sincere, curious voice.

"Well, I don't know," I stammered. "Because...because...you don't know the timing. A wedding you can plan in advance because you know the day. In dying, you don't know. Besides, I may never let you go."

He smiled at that last comment. "I think I do know the date, Jack. And you do too; otherwise you wouldn't all be here."

He smiled again. "I feel great today. As good as I have in months. I think it is my body giving me one last hurrah. I'm going to burn as bright as possible, then go out. Kind of a cool trick if you can pull it off. In the days I have left, we're going to have a graaand time."

"A graaand time doing what?" I asked.

"Oh, lots of things. A tour of my brewery, especially the new facility, great dinners, and one last Sunday brunch with beans-n-chips and Irish porridge. A very *special* brunch."

His emphasis on special caught my attention and I could see the mischievous glint in his eyes.

"What are you planning, Elton? I know you're up to something."

"Nothing much, Jack. Just a little, well, theme brunch, you might say."

"Theme brunch? What is a theme brunch?"

"Like a theme party. You pick the theme of the party and everyone shows up wearing something that relates to that theme. Only we'll do it over brunch."

I didn't even realize my head was shaking until Elton reached out and stopped it, a big smile on his face. "Don't shake your head. I'm a dying man, I get all my last wishes."

"I didn't mean to, Elton, but come on, I'm not the dress up type."

"Just this one last time, Jackie boy. Please."

He had me and he knew it. "Oh, all right, what do I have to dress up as?"

"Well, we're doing an Alice in Wonderland theme, and I'd like you to be the White Rabbit. You'll be so cute hopping around in white fuzzy slippers with little whiskers painted on your nose."

I looked at him incredulously. "The White Rabbit?"

"Yeah, I'll give you my pocket watch and you can run around saying, 'I'm late, I'm late, for a very important date.' It will be almost like being at work."

I continued to stare, unable to speak. Images of me in bunny slippers and whiskers flashed through my head. "Elton, this is not exactly a dignified outfit for..." I saw him trying to suppress his laughter and I knew I had been duped.

"Oh, Jack, you should have seen your face. The White Rabbit indeed."

I started laughing and reached out to cuff him. "Are you ever going to stop yanking my chain, Elton?"

"Not in this lifetime. And probably not in the next one, either." He stood up. "I need a rest now. I'll leave you to ponder the real theme...the seventies."

"The seventies?"

"Righto. We'll dress in our old seventies duds, just like when we first met."

"I didn't bring any seventies clothes with me, so I guess I'll just wear this stuff I have on and say 'right on' and 'cool' a lot."

"Not so fast. MJ is bringing some of your old clothes for you."

"My old clothes? Where is she getting those?"

"Your closet, I would think," he answered.

"My closet?"

"Yeah, the one in the spare room that you haven't cleaned out in years."

"How's she going to get in the house?"

"The spare key under the rock by the back porch. It's still there, isn't it?"

I nodded. I'd been meaning to hide it a little better, but...

"So MJ is going to my house, letting herself in, and finding some old seventies clothes?"

"That's the plan, Jack. I authorized her to do it. I hope you don't mind. But since I was able to tell everyone else before they came, I didn't want you to be left out."

"No, I don't mind," I began sarcastically. "And God knows, I wouldn't want to miss my chance to be the CEO who looks like a seventies drop-out. Maybe we can take a picture and send it to *Fortune* magazine."

He had started towards his bedroom and turned at that last remark. "You know, that's not a bad idea. A little levity would do some of those business publications good. I'll mention it to Maire." He winked, waved and was gone.

I stared after him. At this stage, I didn't know if he was serious or not. I turned and headed to my bedroom. Maybe I needed a nap, too.

MJ and Sarah arrived, and in an atmosphere that ranged from somber to party-like, all of us in the "Elton Clan" got to know each other. Each day the surrealistic nature of the experience would hit me and I would hope that it was only a dream. But each morning I woke and the dream was reality.

Sunday dawned, and after lingering in the shower thinking about the old days at The Gatehouse, I finally stepped out and dried off, a quick task in the dry air of Arizona. I wrapped the towel around me and headed back to my room to get ready for "theme brunch day." Elton had commanded a day of food, fun and cheer. Today I was going to try and follow orders. I started laughing as I looked at the clothes laid out on my bed. My old clothes from the seventies. MJ had scrounged around in my closets, and sure enough, there were some "snappy" twenty-year-old duds in there. One thing about not moving much, I never had to clean out my closets, or get rid of old junk. I knew this was not a good trait, but it served the purpose today, for I looked "fine" in my bell-bottoms, desert boots, funky shirt and vest.

I did a little disco step to the kitchen, poured a glass of orange juice and headed out to the backyard. It was a beautiful morning, around 65 degrees, and I settled into a chair in front of the new waterfall. I watched the water cascading over the rocks into the pool below, then closed my eyes and just listened to the melody. Suddenly, I heard another sound. It was not loud, but it stood out from the sounds of the waterfall. I opened my eyes and looked out over the lawn. There—her right hand high in the air, the left touching the ground—was Sarah. Her head was down by her left knee but tilted up and her eyes seemed to be searching the sky. This was clearly some kind of yoga type exercise and my muscles cringed just looking at the stretches her body was doing. I started towards her, sipping my juice and admiring her grace and flexibility—not to mention her beauty.

"Good morning, Sarah," I called out. She turned her head towards me, leaving her hands where they were and her head by her knee.

"Hi Jack," she said, and her face broke out in a big smile. I liked that, but then the smile got bigger and bigger until finally she started laughing, lost her balance and tumbled over to the ground. I wasn't sure what to make of her actions and her laughter was only getting louder. About the time my neck started to redden and I felt I should, perhaps, get a bit indignant, her hand lifted up and pointed towards me. Bewildered, I tried to figure out what she was pointing at. Her finger moved up and down, as if indicating something on me, and finally I looked down at myself. I saw my forty-something body housed in bell-bottoms, funky shirt, and vest—all just a shade too small for my current build. I sat on the edge of the gazebo and waited for the peals of laughter to stop.

"Sorry to interrupt your exercise, Sarah. But I'm happy to be able to provide you with free entertainment, even at my expense."

"I'm sorry, Jack," she said, "I know it's not polite to laugh at someone. But it really isn't you; it's those clothes. My God, I can't believe we wore that stuff. And I really can't believe you ever wore it. It seemed like you were the conservative dresser among us."

"Yes, well, I had my moments in the seventies, too." I turned in my best GQ modeling pose. "I don't think I look too bad. I may start a new trend here."

She laughed again, shaking her head. "I don't think so, Jack, and after today, retire those things for good. I don't believe they'll qualify for any trends soon. Especially not CEO dress trends."

"I'll retire mine if you'll retire yours," I said. "Let's have a bonfire at The Gatehouse, take off all our clothes and throw them in."

Sarah arched an eyebrow. "Well, that is an interesting proposition."

My heart rate jumped instantly to 180 beats a minute. I was not a flirtatious type, especially around Sarah. But the bonfire invitation had slipped out before I had a chance to choke. We looked at each other. My lips and tongue were frozen now, but luckily for me the onus was on her this time. How would she respond?

She reached for her sweatshirt on the ground, her eyes never leaving me, grabbed it and started for the house. As she passed by—ever so close—she leaned towards me and looked right in my eyes.

"I dare you," she said playfully, and then burst out laughing as she kept walking, looking back at me. Her eyes followed me for several more steps, then she turned and was gone. I sat heavily on the grass, the instant layer of sweat I had just produced glistening in the dawn. I lay back trying to get some air and looked at the sky. Elton, Sarah, CEO—I was close to overload and my emotions were swirling. I felt good about Sarah, and I felt guilty about feeling good about Sarah with Elton so ill. I was proud about being a CEO, but uncertain as to whether I really deserved it. When I engaged in my daily telephone conferences with the office I felt good about being responsible, in charge and devoted to my company; at the same time, the guilt of focusing on work while my best friend was dying weighed on me. Should I be doing more? Was I letting Elton down?

He had told me that he wanted me to help him in these last weeks. I wasn't sure I had. Mostly I felt he was teaching me. One lesson after another. Too many and too fast for me to assimilate, but I was filing them away. I needed quiet and reflection time to really learn, that's why early mornings in the hammock, or watching sunsets out my office windows were so important to me.

I pushed myself up, checking my bell-bottoms for grass stains. They looked fine, but suddenly I wasn't so hot. I had psyched myself up for this brunch, determined to make this last event a happy, joyous one for Elton. Deep in my gut, though, the heaviness was returning: the dense, dark fear of death. Elton seemed to have conquered it, and his example showed so much to me; but many times a day just a thought, a feeling or a sound could trigger the fear again, and it would strike swiftly and without warning. I took several deep breaths and focused back on Elton's words. He had said death is really a birth, a celebrated event as we remembered our spiritual roots and our soul re-joined the Oneness. I still wasn't entirely sure what the Oneness consisted of, but I always felt peace and truth as we talked of this subject. Now my own soul seemed to remember, and for the moment the fear subsided. I started back for the house to re-fill my orange juice determined once again to make this brunch memorable— and to be there for Elton in his coming re-birth, a re-birth that was arriving ever so quickly...

The brunch went fine, with much laughter amidst all the tie-dye, platform shoes, and huge bell-bottoms. I did pretty well, but my condition was fragile, and the reality of Elton's condition was closing in on me fast. It was clear he didn't have much time, and I was struggling to cope. A few days later it became clear that the end was near. Later that night he asked for me to come to his room. I sat next to his bed and leaned forward.

"Hi, Jack," he said. His voice was weak but clear and a smile was on his lips. "How are you today?"

I smiled, my head shaking at the irony. "Elton, this is surrealistic. You're almost..." I struggled to actually say the word and finally chose another euphemism, "...gone, and yet you're smiling, concerned about me, looking like this is just another day at the office."

"Interesting choice of words, Jack. I guess you might say this *is* another day at the office. The office of life, so to speak, and I have done my work and am getting ready for retirement. That brings sadness at all the things I will miss about that life, but at the same time excitement and wonder about all the new experiences in my new life." He looked at me and touched my hand. "I am truly not afraid of this transition, Jack. I am sad about leaving Maire, my family, you and MJ and Sarah and other special people on this earth. But I know I will see you again, so my sadness is tempered. And I am excited about what I will see in the spiritual realm. What a trip! Better than any vacation, I imagine."

"You are really sure about this other life, Elton?"

"Absolutely. I have seen so much evidence of it in my life here, plus in meditations and prayer. A deep knowing has taken root in me, and I have no doubts. So don't worry about me. Let's talk about you."

I shook my head again. "Elton, you're amazing. All right, let's talk about me. What is it about me we should talk about?"

"First, I want to tell you I love you. You've been a most special friend." My eyes immediately welled up. He grasped my hand. "It's true. And I shall look forward to when we meet again." His eyes twinkled. "But I won't root for that to happen too soon."

I smiled through my tears. "Thanks for that. I don't think I am as ready as you for the 'transition.'"

"There are a few favors I want to ask of you."

"You name it."

"First, at the wake, I would like you to finish the ceremony."

"Finish it?"

"Yes, be the grand finale. Maire will lead the wake, and there will be lots of singing, good food, Full Spirit brews, and good times. She will plan the timing of events, but there will be a part where people talk about what a great fellow I was. That should be fun! At the end of all that, I want you as the final speaker."

"What do you want me to say?"

"Whatever is in your heart, Jackman. The only requirement is that you finish with this song. I want people to know I am there and how I feel." He handed me an envelope. "The song and the words are in there. You'll recognize it."

I started to open the envelope.

"Not here," he said. "Open it later. I have one more thing to discuss with you now."

I set the envelope aside, scanned his thin face and finally focused on his eyes, still warm and generous.

"You, Jack, are in a part of your life where everything seems to be coming to a head. You have great pressure on you at work, your personal life seems to be stalled, and of course my situation is not reducing your stress any."

I nodded. "That about sums it up. Any advice?"

"Actually, yes. Listen to yourself. Get very quiet and listen to your inner voice. I think you know what to do. But the pressure from outside forces and the expectations of the world—whether that be society, the Board of Directors, your VPs, family, friends, whatever—they can all cause you to do things that may not be right for you, or your company, or the world. Don't let that happen. And move, Jack, move. You may not have much time."

I hugged him gently. "You know how much I need you, don't you Elton?"

He smiled. "I think one of my roles on this earth has been to be with you, Jack. Now my role is changing, as is yours. And your role is critical. Running a company with all those people, and touching the lives of so many more through suppliers, customers, and the community is a big responsibility." He squeezed my hand again. "I know you are up to it. And I know you will get your personal life the way you want it also."

"You do?" I asked, thinking of Sarah. I was certainly more confident in my work life than in my personal life.

"Yes, I do. And I have one more little surprise that may help with both."

"What is it?"

He smiled again shaking his head. "Not telling, it's a surprise. But it will take about four days of your time and I know you are already behind at work. Can you spare a few more days?"

I nodded. He could have asked me anything and I would have done it.

"Wonderful," he said. "More details later." He squeezed my hand once again. "Give me one more hug and kiss, Jackman, and send in Sarah."

I did as I was told, staining his sheets with my tears as I hugged him.

Later that night, Elton made his transition. He seemed extraordinarily peaceful and ready for the next stage of his life—his spiritual life. He had no doubts that what was to come next would be incredible. A lot of that peacefulness rubbed off on the rest of us, but I was still scared and unwilling to let him go. I prayed continually for a miracle, holding out hope against all odds that somehow he would recover.

Late that night when I finally sat on my bed, exhausted and out of tears, I picked up the envelope Elton had given me. Inside was a short note.

> *Jack: I am honored that you have agreed to be the last speaker at my wake. Say whatever is in your heart and let all those present know that I will be there with them. Then lead everyone in singing the enclosed song. It expresses what I will be feeling at that time.*
>
> *Love,*
>
> *Elton*

I unfolded the other piece of paper and looked at the song. *I Can See Clearly Now*, by Johnny Nash. Elton had always loved that song. I leaned back on the bed, closed my eyes, and tried to see Elton. He had to be there somewhere, but the harder I squeezed the more blackness I saw. Finally, colors started to flash before my eyes and I looked into those colors for him. As they swirled and flickered, my exhaustion took over and I passed into sleep, still looking, still hoping, and still needing my best friend.

sixteen

"That was a beautiful story, Jack. Do you see now why you had to tell it?" Sandor asked. "You needed to hear those words again, to hear Elton's clear and positive expectations for his future, and your own connection to his truth. From the pain, from the sorrow, from the ashes, you are stronger."

I reflected on that as I composed myself. I wasn't sure I was stronger yet, but I did feel lighter, perhaps even freer. And I think there was hope bubbling up as well.

"The story is nearing the end, Jack. Continue now with the wake."

Ah, the wake, I thought. Like nothing I had ever been to. "Okay," I said, "the wake."

Elton had been very clear about the wake. It was to be a time of celebration and joy, not sadness and sorrow. Maire was in charge of it, and she and Elton had planned every aspect. She had a long list of items to prepare for the wake, as well as the day's agenda. I was still there as the last speaker.

The new fountain was bubbling and flowing as I slipped through the patio door and into the backyard. As I got closer, I could see by the froth and the distinct aroma that it was indeed Full Spirit Ale cascading over the edge. I sat on the bench next to it and stared at the golden waterfall and the frothy white "surf" down below. Somewhere in there, I thought, there must be some words for me to say today that would really capture the spirit, heart, joy, and total love of Elton. I didn't see any words in the ale, and although I did a lot of public speaking—frequently "off the cuff"—I was beginning to get nervous. I realized how important it was to me to get this "right"—to make sure everyone heard just how incredible a person Elton had been. Why he had asked me to be the last speaker, I didn't know. But I did know that I didn't want to disappoint him. I also knew that so far I had been unable to come up with anything that did Elton justice.

I got up off the bench and headed out behind the fountain towards the gazebo. Elton had put that in a few years back so he'd have a place outside but protected from the sun. He had always kept the Irish love of the outdoors, but he also had the fair Irish skin, and had been smart enough to keep it covered from the desert rays. I continued past the gazebo to the back of Maire and Elton's property. It was a large piece of land, almost two acres, and like many southwest homes, had a big backyard. I wasn't used to this phenomenon. In the San Francisco Bay Area, where land was at a premium, developers would have put at least eight to ten houses on that size lot.

I shook my head to clear it. When I was nervous, I had a habit of losing my focus and becoming distracted. I looked around at the backyard and laughed. Comparing lot sizes here to the Silicon Valley certainly fell into the distracted category. There was one thing about Elton's backyard size that did matter, though. How many people could squeeze into a yard that large? And the answer was, as Elton had put it, "a whole mess of em." If there had been chairs set up, we could have just counted them. But Elton's instructions were for the wake to be like a picnic. One last picnic, this time with all his friends, not just the usual four. So there were blankets scattered everywhere, each with a small picnic basket that held fine silverware, linens, and crystal salt and pepper shakers, and a bowl of strawberries for everyone to munch on as they waited for the ceremony to begin. Dessert was strudel, special ordered and flown in from Ingrid's restaurant in Whistler, B.C. And also in the basket, of course, a saying. A saying Father Antonio brought in for the occasion. It was sealed in an envelope with instructions to bring it home and schedule a picnic with your family and friends. And after they eat and lie back looking at the sky for a few moments, they were to open the envelope, read it out loud, and say what they were feeling—thirty seconds, no more—pure, unfiltered feelings.

I took a breath and began walking again, finally stopping in the gazebo. From there I could see people arriving in large numbers. It was almost time to begin. I headed back up front to help welcome the guests. I said one last prayer that I would have the wisdom when I needed it, took a breath and reminded myself that this was a celebration. It was hard to get into a celebration frame of mind, but Elton truly deserved to be honored and celebrated, and I wasn't going to be the one to bring the party down.

A temporary stage had been constructed, and Elton's family sat there along with Sarah, MJ, and me. In the front row was Elton's adoptive family—Hank, Corliss, Mary, Hank Jr., and little Chelsea, only seven when Elton met her but now a beatiful young woman. Seeing her now, so grown and polished, reminded me of all the time that had passed since Elton had arrived in America. I said a silent prayer of thanks that at least I had been blessed by his presence for all those years.

Maire was the master of ceremonies and, finally, she took a deep breath and stepped to the microphone. She started by telling stories about her husband, then invited others up to tell their stories. Family, friends, employees from his brewery, even the mailman—all had Elton stories of love, courage, and fun. Finally, Maire paused, smiled between her tears and looked over at me. I stood up as she turned back to the audience.

"Elton wanted a 'closer' as he called it. Someone to really finish the wake off with a bang. He asked Jack to do the honors."

She stepped back and turned towards me. I got up out of my special director's chair and came to her. We hugged each other tightly, holding on for several seconds. Finally, I let go and stepped to the podium. I looked out at the assembled group but all I saw was fuzz. My red, wet eyes wouldn't focus, and after several futile blinks and gyrations I stopped trying to clear them up. Maybe this would be easier if I was in my own little world. I took a deep breath, leaned slightly against the podium for support, and tilted the microphone up.

"Good day," I began, "or should I say 'brilliant day' as my dearest friend Elton would have said. I don't know why Elton asked me to say the last words here today; many others have more to say than I do. If it's spiritual wisdom he was looking for, I see Sarah and our old friend from Santa Clara, Antonio, who was Father Antonio when we met him and is one of the wisest people I have ever met. And if he wanted laughter and radiance, MJ is sitting right here, too, along with many of Elton's relatives, who all display Elton's wonderful wit and humor. So, as I thought about why he asked me, and, indeed, why he asked me to spend so much time with him in his last months, I could only come up with one reason. He did it for me. He did it to make me think about life and death, and the spiritual wisdom I have been lacking.

"My Mom and Dad tried to impart that to me, as have others over the years, especially Sarah and Antonio, and, of course, Elton. He would try to open my heart to something greater than my job or next promotion, and usually he could crack it a bit...then bosses or customers or employees would call and off I'd go, successfully distracted away from what really mattered. I say successfully because even though I may not have invited the distraction consciously, I welcomed it, and followed it as though it were a Pied Piper with an irresistible tune. And indeed it was irresistible, for without that I would have had to start looking at the real questions of life. And Lord knows that scared me more than any customer or big contract. Elton knew this, and knew that in following the Pied Piper I tread the wrong path.

"And so, in these last few months, and today, he has forced me to face my life. In other words, in his death, he has given me the greatest gift of my life.

"And that act typifies Elton. Service to others, generosity beyond measure. He would not only give you the shirt off his back, he'd wash and iron it first!"

I paused while laughter spread.

"We laugh because that's a funny thought, but for Elton not far off from truth. He gave blood, he gave bone marrow, and his wallet was thick with every organ donation card possible so in case of his untimely death someone would benefit.

"That laughter a few moments ago felt good. And, as Maire said earlier, Elton charged all of us to have a great time today and remember to **celebrate** his life. So, in honor of that request, I'd like to tell a few stories.

"The first has to do with Elton's penchant for getting excited and forgetting a few details. Our first Christmas at The Gatehouse, he came home one day with a bunch of Christmas lights and he wanted to put them up *right* now. It was almost dark, but he wanted to see them shining that night. So, I helped him get the ladder and we laid it against the house and up he went. The Gatehouse is two stories, so he was up a good twenty feet and it was quite dim.

"'Elton,' I called out, 'you had better secure yourself up there so you don't fall off the roof.'

"He looked impatient, but said, 'Okay, I'll tie the extension cord around my waist and around the chimney so if I slip and start to slide off the roof, the cord will catch me.'

"'Good thinking,' I said.

"So he tied himself off and began stringing the lights. But as he neared the crest of the roof, he slipped on a mossy patch and began sliding. In those few seconds as he slid, I remember thinking how smart we were to have tied him off to the chimney. Then I watched him careen over the edge, off a tree limb, and land with a thud in a bush a few steps from where I stood. As he looked up in pain and bewilderment, a mass of coiled extension cord slid off the roof and dropped over his head like a ring toss at the circus. A small tag on the front of the cord was facing me and I could see it clearly. It said: '50 foot Extension Cord.' Elton could see me mouthing the words and he turned the tag and read it.

"'Jack,' he said with a grimace, 'it appears that tying yourself off with a fifty foot cord when you're on a twenty foot roof is a less brilliant solution to stopping a fall than I imagined. Let's chalk this one up as a lesson, and perhaps we won't tell the girls about it, eh? Now help me out of this bush and we can start creating our story of how I got these cuts and bruises stopping two, no three, big lugs from stealing a little old lady's purse.'"

My eyes had cleared as I told the story and I could see the crowd laughing. I could also see several whispering what no doubt were similar Elton stories of unbounded enthusiasm getting him into a scrape—sometimes literally.

God, I loved Elton then, and the feelings were pure, unfiltered by me and unfettered by the weight of what was supposed to be. It just was, deep within me, and nothing could change that. Not even death. My eyes welled up with the power and richness of the emotion and I started speaking—a flow of words that reflected long-suppressed feelings and the many discussions Elton and I had had recently as we pondered the real questions of life.

"I loved Elton…I mean I love Elton, for I know he is still with us. Elton and I have talked a lot these last few weeks and we have read some wonderful works. One of our favorites was *The Prophet* by Kahlil Gibran. One passage goes like this:

'For life and death are one, even as the river and sea are one.'

"Elton is with us, he has just moved into the sea and we cannot fathom his strength now, or his joy.

'For when the earth shall claim your limbs, then shall you truly dance.'

"That's also from Gibran and I know Elton is dancing now as he's never danced before." I smiled.

"It has got to be the greatest Irish jig ever jigged." I paused and looked up. "Keep dancing Elton, I love you."

I had to stop again and take a breath. These were alternately the happiest and hardest moments of my life.

"Everyone stand, please. Look up, raise your hands up, and sing to Elton a prayer from his homeland. The words are on the gold sheets you should have on your blankets. If you don't have one, just listen, you'll pick it up quick. I'll lead you.

"May the road rise up to meet you

May the wind be always at your back

May the sun shine warm upon your face

May the rain fall gently on your fields

Until we meet again

May God hold you

In the hollow of His hand

"Once more. Everybody together now.

"May the road rise up to meet you

May the wind be always at your back

May the sun shine warm upon your face

May the rain fall gently on your fields

Until we meet again

May God hold you

In the hollow of Her hand

And we sang again and again, me leading and a few Irish musicians carrying the melody. We sang to each other, and to Elton, and to the dance of life, the dance that you danced before death, and after. Tears and laughter and hugs spread everywhere, and the air sparkled. I finally stopped, grabbed Maire and Sarah's hands and held them aloft. Just as I was about to speak, Sarah stepped in front of the microphone.

"Before Jack finishes, I have a request from Elton. He asked that after we sing the Irish prayer to each other, we dance an Irish song. At Elton and Maire's wedding there was a song all of us danced to. It was called *When ye go away* and was sung by an Irish lad named Mike Scott. He is now the lead singer and writer for the Irish group The Waterboys and he has recorded that song. Elton would like all of us to dance with each other and with him." She handed a sound technician a CD and the music started.

Suddenly, the wedding seemed like yesterday as the memories of that dance with Sarah flooded back. I held out my hand to her. She took it and we began to dance. I looked out over the yard and everyone was dancing—young, old, male, female, all combinations, sizes and shapes. Next to us on the stage MJ and Maire danced, smiles and tears mixing as they gently turned. It was an incredible experience and my emotions were so strong and coming from so many different directions that finally I just held on to Sarah and let the song wash over me. As it ended Sarah hugged me and stepped back to the microphone.

"One last thing," she said. "At the wedding Elton took the stage after this song and told Maire that he would not EVER go away and that she made him the happiest man on earth. He wanted me to pass on to her that he did not go away, he is still around and would always be with her. And now she has made him the happiest spirit in the Universe."

Sarah backed away and let her words echo over the yard. Maire was laughing and crying at the same time, still holding on to MJ for support. Sarah moved back in to the microphone.

"It is time for the grand finale as Elton would say. Here's Jack."

I took a few deep breaths and tried to clear my throat. I reached for Maire's hand, then Sarah's.

"Join hands, please. Elton himself requested our last celebration. As he was dying, and as most of us felt sorry for him and bemoaned his fate, he hummed, sang, and played a song on the stereo. It was a song he had always liked, and in those last weeks it really spoke to him. But he also said the song would capture his feelings perfectly now. RIGHT NOW! He wanted you all to hear it and sing it with him. MJ, kick on the power and turn it up. Ladies and gentlemen, I give you Elton, speaking through Johnny Nash!"

And out it came, the clear sweet voice of Johnny Nash singing *I Can See Clearly Now*. The music was joyous and I could almost hear Elton coming through, arms upraised, singing in joy.

"Hear the words," I shouted above the music. "Elton wants you to know that the rain is gone, the pain is gone, and it truly is a bright, bright, sunshiny day!"

I let go to the feeling and sang in praise, love and tears.

The celebration continued with food, stories, laughter, hugs, and of course Full Spirit Ale. Elton sure knew how to throw a party. Even when his presence was only ethereal.

MJ, Sarah and I stayed another day to help Maire with the clean up and just to be with her. She insisted on taking us to the airport the following day. I mean, really insisted. And we found out why as we said our goodbyes in the terminal. She hugged each of us, and in the midst of tears and wistful smiles, she reached into her oversized purse and pulled out four envelopes. She pulled our hands together in the center of the circle and looked up at our quizzical faces.

"Elton is nothing if not dramatic, as all of you know. He has one last surprise for you. He would like you to take your envelope home with you, get in your favorite spot—in front of the fire, outside as the dawn breaks or the sun sets magnificently, wherever you are most peaceful and centered—and then open the envelope. He has some requests in there and he would like you to indulge him this one last time." She looked at the envelopes and handed us each one with our name on it. As I took mine, my face broke out into a wide grin. The others looked over at me.

"That guy just brings me joy," I explained. "It's one surprise after the other. He creates more dramatic tension than any ten people I know. He should have been a novelist." I studied my envelope. "He wants me to wait until I get home and am in my peaceful, centered spot? I'll be lucky if I make it to my plane."

Maire leaned over and hugged me. "Speaking of planes, all of you had better get going. And I am confident that you have the will power to wait to open your envelopes." She paused and held my eyes. "I will need more of an assurance from you Jack. You see," and she waved the fourth envelope in front of me, "this is supposed to go with you. But it is not to be opened until a very special time, because it is for all of you."

Now my curiosity was peaking. "When can I open that one?"

"You will find out. But you must promise to wait and open the envelopes at the appointed times. Do you agree?"

"Oh, come on, Maire. I have always been a patient guy, but isn't this beyond the call."

"Do you agree, Jack?" Maire repeated.

"Just a little peek," I whined, but by now I was smiling and Maire knew she had won.

"No peeks," she said as she handed me the fourth envelope, a thick one. She hugged Sarah and MJ and stepped back.

"Now go. I love you all." Her misty eyes twinkled mischievously as she backed up slowly. "And do call me after you have opened all the envelopes. I can't wait to hear about them." With that she turned and was gone.

The three of us looked at each other. Finally, MJ stepped forward and hugged and kissed us. "I am going to miss my plane if I don't get going. I love you both. I will see you soon, I hope, and judging from Maire's comments, maybe sooner than I think. Jack," she said as she turned and started off, "don't open anything early or I will come down and do the hamper torture on you."

"The hamper torture?"

"That's the one I used to do to my brother where I stuffed him in an old pink metal hamper and sat on the lid. At your size, you'd be harder to get in the hamper, but..." By now she was almost shouting she was so far away. "Bye," she called and blew us a kiss.

Sarah and I watched her hurry away then turned towards each other simultaneously. Our eyes met. Immediately my palms started sweating. With Elton's illness, my focus had been on him, as was Sarah's. We had spent some time together but usually in a group or to plan some aspect of the activities. Suddenly, my feelings for Sarah welled up, and our last conversation after her clinic opening came to mind. She had said then that we should spend more time together, but I hadn't followed up. First, I was scared and just procrastinating, then I had been promoted to CEO, and then Elton had gotten sick. I could defend my inaction, but the bottom line was I was letting something slip away that was very important to me. Our flirtatious backyard conversation with my seventies clothes on had been a start, and the dance at the wake was truly special, but if I didn't follow up I would be right back where I started.

Sarah was looking at me curiously. My face was giving me away again. "Jack, is there something you need to say?"

I felt myself choking again. My throat tightened, my brain locked, the words stuck.

"I've got to go," she finally said.

I could see her slipping away again and with all the courage and strength I could muster, I spoke. "No, wait. Please, just a second. In Elton's backyard, the bonfire with our clothes? You said we could talk more later. And after your clinic opening you said we should spend more time together. Do you still feel that way?"

Her eyes flared. I could see she was irritated.

"I don't know, Jack. I mean, I think so, but I'm confused. Frankly, I am never very sure where you are coming from, or why there are such long gaps between your calls. It seems to me that your business goals are the number one priority in your life, and that's fine. You need to follow your own path." She paused. "You have a wonderful heart, and I can see so many possibilities and such potential. But I don't want to be involved with potential. That's why I think we need to spend time together. Are you willing to make that commitment, to at least spend some time together?"

I nodded feverishly. At least with that question, I did not have to speak.

She reached for my hands. I quickly wiped them on my pants. Damn, why did they have to sweat at the most inopportune times?

"Jack, I know this has been a very hard time for you. Elton was special to all of us, but I know he was your closest friend, someone you could confide in, and learn from. He asked you to do a lot these last few months and he pushed you to learn about life. I have seen some wonderful growth in you. Amidst the tragedy and the pain, you have arisen stronger. As you head back into your very difficult job, remember all that you have learned. It was a wonderful gift from Elton."

I nodded, tears forming and releasing in my eyes. My emotions were bouncing so hard I thought they might snap. I was so happy that Sarah and I could discuss and agree to work on our relationship, to at least give it a chance to blossom; on the other hand, Elton's loss cast everything in a bittersweet light, and if I let my mind go there I was still overwhelmed with grief.

Sarah moved forward and took me in her arms. My tension released and I leaned against her for support. She held me as I fought with my emotions, then she turned her head up and kissed me lightly on the lips.

"Goodbye. Be well, and take care of yourself and your spirit. My recommendation as a doctor is for you to take a few days off and recover from these last few months." She looked in my eyes. "I know what you are thinking, and it is true you have been gone from work for quite a while. But trust me, you need some time to get whole again." She stepped back and cocked her head.

"And my recommendation as a very close friend is that you remember our conversation and act accordingly." She paused and held her letter up. "Somehow I think these may help." She touched my arm and started away, stopping after about fifteen feet. "Let me know what spot you choose that is the most peaceful and centering for you. I'm curious." My eyes followed her across the termi-nal until she was lost amongst the scurrying travelers.

I looked around. I was standing alone in the middle of the terminal complex. In the past I think I would have felt alone, even though I was surrounded by thousands of people. Today, howev-er, I did not feel alone. With all I had learned from Elton, plus his two envelopes in my hand—and now a message of hope from Sarah—I felt connected. Not only to them, but also to everyone. I felt a connection to humanity then, with the common experi-ences we all have and must deal with, like love, death, and fami-ly. Watching the people hurry by, I knew there was a story there for each one, of courage, dignity, pain and ultimately, love.

I took a deep, hopeful breath, tucked the letters into my bag, and moved into the throng of humanity. Another story on its way to the next act.

chapter seventeen

"Sandor," I called out, "I want to go on with the story. You'll love Elton's little surprise. Sandor? Sandor? Hey, I hope you're not on a bathroom break, because I am starting anyway. We are getting close to the present, I think, and maybe somewhere in here I will figure out where I am now, and who you are." I was getting excited at that thought. Enough with this limbo state. "Listen up, big guy, here we go."

There was never any doubt as to where I would open the letter. I returned to The Gatehouse, slept lightly amidst a swirl of dreams and visions, then arose at dawn and went out to the hammock—Elton's hammock. Softly, I said "Hello, Elton" as I settled in, sending my words up towards the yellows and reds spreading across the sky. I breathed in a full dose of the morning air and opened the letter.

Hi Jack!

Did you make it back to The Gatehouse, or are you opening this on the plane? Well, either way I love you.

I have a request for you, Jackman. I'd like you to take a long weekend next week. And go to Ireland. Yes, you read it right: Ireland. I would like you and MJ and Sarah to accompany Maire there as she returns to our homeland to participate in the ceremonies honoring me. You would be a great support and comfort to her, especially during the long flights and layovers. Then I'd like you to do one more thing.

Get up at dawn the morning following the ceremony and take the extra letter Maire gave you. You will be staying at The

Fitzpatrick Castle Hotel again—where Maire and I got married you'll remember—and at the top of the hillside above the hotel, there is a clearing with a stunning view. Go to the clearing with MJ and Sarah, get comfortable and then open that envelope and read it aloud. It will be my chance to speak with you one last time.

Plane tickets and confirmation numbers for the hotel are enclosed. Hope to see you there, Jack.

Love,

Elton

Of course we all went. The flights were long, but we traded stories and played cribbage amidst the bad food and plastic cups of orange juice and club soda. The ceremony was touching and poignant, and the Irish celebration of life was strong. We reacquainted ourselves with members of Elton and Maire's families, and walked through the neighborhood listening to stories of childhood escapades. Finally, Maire dropped us back at Fitzpatrick Castle and wished us well. It was clear she knew we were in for something special. We went to bed one more time, wondering what surprises Elton had in store for us.

We arose in the darkness before dawn and wound our way up the hillside. At the top, the hill flattened into a small plateau that narrowed as it reached for the Irish Sea. A castle tower stood high on the cliff; it looked exactly like a rook on a chessboard. It was well placed, for nothing could reach Ireland by sea along that coast without the tower having sight of it. A beautiful bay stretched to the south and west, and the inter-city train rolled around the bay by the water's edge, mixing the rhythms of the ocean with the turning of the wheels. Dublin lay quietly to the north, cathedral spires dotting the horizon as the most visible features of its landscape. As the sun crept over the horizon, speckling the thin cloud layer with pinks and golds, we laid our blankets down and stood watching nature's finest show. Those first rays of light seemed to seek us out, and I realized that, just as in our Irish prayer at Elton's wake, the wind was blowing gently at our backs, while the sun shone warm upon our face. It was as if all the spiritual power in the world was centered on that hill and in our little circle. I felt the power and love as MJ, Sarah and I grasped hands to close the circle. We stood motionless as the warmth spread through us and the vortex of power continued to build. Finally, we sat together, still holding each other's hands, and I opened the envelope I had received at the airport. Inside was a letter. From Elton. To all of us.

> *Good Morning to my closest and dearest friends, or should I say Brilliant Morning on this fine Irish dawn:*
>
> *I have been thinking back lately to that first day we met. At Dynamics, in the orientation room, waiting for the instructor to show up, making a little small talk and then MJ leading us on a break to the doughnut shop. The conversation there was astonishing. Four disparate individuals meeting for the first time, and yet it was as if I was home. I remember the pure joy I felt as I left the shop: I knew this was something special. And my instincts were as right as they ever were in my whole life. I cannot imagine my life without your participation in it. It has been full and wonderful, and I would not trade it for anything or anyone else's life. Thank you all!*
>
> *Now, on to the meat of the letter. As you read this, of course, I am already gone. (At least physically, although I may be around in another sense...but more on that later). I had expected to have another 25-30 years to get all my thoughts out on life and business. Now I have only this letter left. So please bear with me if I get a little long-winded today. (I know what you are thinking, Jack, I am always long-winded).*

I had to stop reading here because my eyes just couldn't focus any more. In fact, I had been thinking of all the times I had encouraged Elton to "get to the point." He and I were total opposites in that respect. I wanted the facts, the data, the bottom line. Elton told the whole story, not only the facts, but also the feelings, the people, the personalities, the history, the possible interactions and outside forces. Nowadays, we call that systems thinking and pay top dollar for it. I had always learned a lot from listening to Elton, even if I was frustrated by the time it took him to get to the bottom line. Now though, as I read his letter, I wanted him to be as long-winded and verbose as possible. As the words came out of my mouth, they were his words and I felt as if he were still there with us. I didn't want that letter to ever end...I wiped my eyes and continued reading.

> *Well, after all these years of us discussing life and work, leader-ship and friendship, from those early days when we thought we knew it all, to the last few years when we finally started to know how much we didn't know; after all those heated debates, you didn't think I would leave you without one last soliloquy, did you? For all that you've given me over the years, I'd like to give you my philosophy on friend-ship, leadership, and life. As you see, it's all the same thing: leading with soul. I especially owe you some thoughts, Jack. You asked me to help you understand the things I was doing at Full Spirit and help you start implementing some of those principles at Dynamics. Well, I can't help with actual implementation, but maybe this will help. It's a culmination of all my experiences and all the reading and research I've done, especially the intense work to get ready for the brewery. So, here they are—Elton's Principles of Leadership: How to lead your life with heart and soul.*

Elton's Principles of Leadership

1) *Lead with your heart. Simply put, don't be afraid to let your heart show. Your heart cares, and if you think that to be a successful leader you must put it away, you are wrong. If you think you need to be a "tough" manager, you may be right. Maybe the situation calls for tough steps. But if you think that means you can't let your heart out, you are wrong. How many times have you heard someone talk about seeing the boss perform a caring act, and being surprised that he or she would do some-thing like that? Surprised, then usually impressed, even a bit respectful. The truth is that we want to work for and with people who are very human, who have a large heart, who feel when they make decisions. We may not like all of their decisions, but if we think they feel our pain, our fear, then at least we know they didn't come to those decisions lightly. It is a misnomer of western business that we must not feel, that all our meetings and decisions must be filled only with logic and facts. Let your heart in, too.*

And by the way, this makes you much more attractive to customers, and even suppliers. The caring and personality that comes from the heart is infectious.

2) *People come first. Really. Truly. No joke.* And it's not just a nice saying, not just good wallpaper for those executive boardrooms, not just a good lead for this year's vision statement. It is damn true (you know I'm serious about this if I swear). Include them in all your thoughts. Not just because you are scared they will strike or quit, but also because thinking of them first will produce good long-range decisions—and because you truly care about them. And if you don't truly care about them, go back to number 1 above and open up your heart. And remember, as you care about them, they will start to care about you. And you need that as a boss. You need it for your own soul, you need it to work with them through the tough times, and it is that caring that will start to build good will for you. Just as you build good will in customers and communities, you need to build it with the employees. So they cut you some slack when you're having a bad day. So they don't judge you for your every action, or lack of action. So that you all stand together and weather the bad times—and rejoice in the good.

3) *Value people's thinking and creativity.* This seems obvious, but let me give you a couple of examples of it not happening. First, in our education systems, kindergarten through college, how many thinking or creativity classes are taught? Very few. So, there isn't much value placed on it in school, is there? Second question: Have you ever been in a meeting at work where you, or another, brought forward an idea only to have it attacked by the other members of the meeting and all the negative points raised without any corresponding benefits brought up? How did you feel? Did it make you want to jump up and throw some more ideas on the table? Or did you retreat a bit, holding back bold, innovative thinking in favor of conservative, incremental input? For your organization, make sure everyone knows that you value their thinking and their new ideas. And that a wild idea isn't "stupid" or "crazy," but, rather, a starting point to trigger

other minds to move from the wild, perhaps unworkable idea, to the fresh, creative idea that breaks you out of the pack.

4) Diversity is very good for business (remember my slogan—Hire an Irishman!). Okay, I am just kidding about the Irishman thing, but not about diversity. And not for the reasons you may suspect. I am not talking about filling quotas, or trying to meet regulations and guidelines so the company doesn't get in trouble. I am talking about leveraging the value of the minds, hearts and souls of the company. In the last bullet, I discussed a wild idea triggering the thoughts of another, then that may trigger someone else, and so on, until perhaps a breakthrough is reached. Moving from one idea—crazy or not—to others is very powerful, and something the mind does very well. The brain is very good at associating from something it is not familiar with back to the familiar. Or, in an idea session, from one idea or random input, back towards the problem to be solved or purpose of the meeting. And when we associate, we do it in OUR minds, based on OUR experiences, education, culture, and so on. Thus, a diverse group will by nature produce richer, more robust output. So it is a good business decision to be diverse, regardless of what any one else thinks.

5) Focus on front-line management. All levels of management are obviously important (try not to have too many though), but it is the front-line managers that must hire, train, mentor, discipline, promote and grow the front-line workers. Also, the front-line managers are the face of the company to the workers. I found that out the hard way at the brewery when we lost three employees in one department in six months. I thought I had done all the right things in being progressive in our pay, vacation, time off for community service, 401K plans and so on. I was so busy I didn't pay much attention at first to losing a few employees, but after the third one I began to wonder. My research and interviews showed they quit because of their manager. My policies—and me personally—didn't make any difference when they had to spend most of their time around a poor manager they didn't like or respect. And they probably figured that if I allowed that kind of bad management, then good policies or not, I probably wasn't

much better. So make sure you get the right people into management—not necessarily the best technical person, but the best
manager and leader—and then grow, train and mentor them to
be the best manager and leader they can be. (You may see the
underlying corollary there. You must have an upward path for
your technical folks; otherwise, they will naturally aspire to be
managers if that is the only way to be promoted. That can be a
very costly situation—you lose the day to day technical expert-
ise, and you often gain a bad manager.)

6) Treat people individually, like they are different—because they
are! I had a friend growing up who had three brothers. Their
mom used to say, "The boys all must be treated the same. That's
the only fair thing." She meant well, but the boys were different.
Some matured faster and could be given more responsibility at a
younger age; some loved the family business and wanted to be
there; some loved athletics, others music or reading; some wanted
to "get out in the world" right away, others wanted to go to the
University and be scholars. The family had a lot of conflict and
rebellion over what "the boys" were allowed, encouraged, or
forced to do based on what another sibling had done.

In business, we sometimes do the same thing, forcing people
to follow some corporate mold, job description, or policy without
regard for their unique skills, talents, and preferences. As simple a
thing as work hours is often overlooked. If you have flexibility
there, use it. Jack, you're up and out of bed and doing great work
by 6:30 am. MJ is definitely not a morning person (you might
even call her scary in the early morning), but gets stronger
throughout the day and often does brilliant work late at night.
Making them both follow a nine-to-five schedule sounds dumb—
and is! But we do it all the time in business. You might be thinking, "I don't. Our work schedules are flexible." But what about
the other skills and talents of your employees? Do you use them
to their best advantage? Do you even know what those other skills
and talents are? Taking the time to know the people working for
you and then putting them in positions to best utilize their natural abilities and talents is perhaps the most critical job of a

manager. And when those people are in the right position, they excel, they get more energized, and—if they are treated right by their manager and company—they are well on their way to loving their job, their organization, and their company. And people who are energized, excited, even passionate about their job—and who love their work, organization, and company—are the most critical element to long term company performance.

Jack, a special message for you. You are in a big company. Changes such as these will not come easy, either for you or the company. Remember that there will be thorns. There will be those in the company who hang on to old ways and refuse to let go. Be understanding with them; they made their mark in the company using those old ways. Persevere and continue to invite them to change. But if they will not, allow them to go. And don't fear their departure. Just as a tree renews itself, so shall you. Don't be afraid to let go of your leaves. This opens up space for new leaves, and ideas, to grow. And, personally, do not fear shedding your own leaves. They will fall, turn brown and provide new fuel for you—just as leaves do for the earth. And your own new leaves will blossom.

That is all I have on leadership. I was a CEO only a short time, but my learning was enormous. Each day was incredible, as new insight came my way. I hope it helps each of you, and anyone you may give it to.

But I am not done yet, my good friends. I have many things on my mind today.

You three are so special to me. I want to give you everything I have: my love, my learning, and my insights, the special truths that began to well up in my last days. You may not need the insights personally, but perhaps you can be the conduit to bring them to those who do need them.

You know, when people prepare to die, they begin to have a different perspective on living. Things that seemed important before don't seem so now. Worries and concerns shift pretty quickly. Broken cars, traffic tickets and gum surgery seem pretty trivial all of a sudden. And as you realize that, you suddenly have much more time to think about things that are important. Like bettering your relationships, helping others, finding and fulfilling your life's purpose. Remember that quote from Buddha (MJ, I first saw it in your letter to all of us from England when you started working at The Body Shop, thank you)— "Your work is to discover your work, and then with all your heart to give yourself to it." It's true. We all do have a purpose in life. A contract, if you will, and we signed it before we came here. When we are working in that contract we are happy and fulfilled, and life is a joyous experience. I'm not saying there won't be trials and problems to work through, but when you are in your work—Joseph Campbell would say, "following your bliss"—you have inner strength, joy, and contentment. And when you are not, you feel it. It could be a vague uneasiness, depression, or downright misery.

We have so many examples in society that the things that are supposed to make us happy really don't. Money, fame, power, all call out to us...and too often we follow. But newspapers and television are full of examples of people with all those things who are not happy. Drugs, abuse, suicide — these are very prevalent in those circles. And you yourself know that happiness or fulfillment doesn't come from those external things. You can get that promotion, or make a little extra money, or get the partner you have wanted. But after the initial celebration and a little time of satisfaction, you return to your previous state. Why? I believe it is because an inner spiritual core is lacking.

A spiritual core doesn't have anything to do with religion, although if you have one that suits you, that's fine. It has to do with purpose in your life, with an understanding and pursuit of your life's contract, with the recognition that you are part of a greater whole, and you have a part to play as the universe unfolds. It is a focusing within, not without, and it requires courage and dedication and the willingness to accept that you don't know all the answers. This can be scary. Pursuing those types of goals is more intimidating than just putting in your forty hours a week. As a result, I think we all find ways to keep us from focusing within, to keep from facing the critical questions of the spirit. Most of the ways are by focusing on external things. I call this being distracted.

We know we should be looking inside, facing our fears, finding our purpose, living our true life and true purpose. But instead we allow ourselves to be distracted by all the other things that life can bring to the table. We become workaholics, languish in destructive or co-dependent relationships, watch TV, go to shows, play video games, get caught up in one trauma-drama after another with family, friends, colleagues; we worry about the past, then we worry about the future, rarely stopping to live, really live, in the present. We say to ourselves that after this trauma, or this problem, or this vacation is over, then I will get on with finding my purpose, and challenging myself to be the person I was meant to be. But guess what? Those things are plentiful in the world. There is a never-ending supply of things with which to distract yourself. Like Old Faithful, they will be popping up constantly. So the challenge comes straight back to you. Will you allow yourself to be distracted, or will you move the distractions aside and focus on your real work?

Now, don't get me wrong. I'm not trying to give the message that going to a show, or watching a little TV, or working a long week is bad. It is only bad if you use it as a distraction from what you know to be your real work. Remember, I started a brewery! I am all in favor of pleasure and joy in your life. In fact, let's talk about pleasure and joy a bit more. As a going away present, more for me than anyone else—this should ensure you don't forget me too soon—I have established some principles. I call them Elton's principles of life. I don't mean to sound preachy with them, but again, if they go through the three of you to the world, maybe they can help the world be a better place. And as you lie dying—at least as I do—thoughts and goals turn broader and the question of how I can help the world becomes much more central. So, here are my principles in the joy and pleasure area.

1) Do only what you love doing.

2) Be with only those you love, admire, learn from, or who help your growth process.

3) Put only things you love into your life.

4) Simplify your life.

Oh, I can hear the shouts of protest going up, and your voices saying:

"We can't only do the things we love, or be with those we love, or admire, or put only things we love into our lives. Come on, Elton, are you nuts? We don't have that kind of control of our lives."

Two points here. I'm just dying, I'm not getting stupid; yes, I recognize there will be things in your life that don't fit the criteria. But, what if you carried those principles close to your heart, and based all of your decisions on them? Do you think the quality of the time you spent "doing and being and putting" would improve dramatically? Yeah, so do I. Let's look at them one at a time.

1) *Do only what you love doing.* Again, I hear you saying that there are so many things we have to do that this is an impossible principle to follow. But how much of what "you have to do," do you really have to do? How much do you do out of a sense of obligation, out of habit, to please someone else, to gain approval? Think about how you make decisions in your life. Bring the things that give you bliss to the forefront. If you are uncertain about how you feel about something, chances are you don't love it. But as you try to decide, listen to your heart, your inner voice, your instincts. As you listen more and more, they will get louder. You will begin to feel more and more certain about your decisions.

2) *Be with only those you love, admire, learn from, or help your growth process.* Similar vein to the first principle. Be with those who further your joy, spiritual advancement, wisdom, learning, and love. Do not spend your valuable time in dysfunctional relationships, stressful relationships, catering to people you don't want to be around, putting up with people because you think it is what you are supposed to do. Don't spend your time with negative people, with negative energy. If you always feel tired and drained after spending time with someone, examine that relationship very hard. Have the courage to look inside and understand what you value, and who supports what you value, and then follow that knowledge.

3) *Put only things you love into your life,* and

4) *Simplify your life.* Principles three and four are so closely aligned that I'll talk about them together. Simplify your life,

simplify your life, simplify your life. Have I said it enough yet? This is critical. Life is so complex these days that we must consciously take steps to simplify, to have those things in our lives that we love, and discard the rest. We are so good at collecting clutter. Our houses are full, our garages are full, our desks are full, and our cabinets are full. Companies have sprung up across the country just to deal with our clutter, selling ways to organize our closets and junk rooms, and systems to deal with all our messes. These may be helpful for organizing, but first, get rid of at least half of your "stuff." Think about why you have it and when you would really use it, then make tough decisions. As you clear physical clutter, you will begin to feel lighter mentally and spiritually as well. And when you have a chance to acquire something, put it through a rigorous test. Make sure you love it before you get it. Don't acquire just to acquire. This gets back to being distracted. Are you buying things as a distraction; are you shopping so you can avoid other areas of your life that need attention? Only bring something into your life that fills you with joy, or peace, or reverence. Otherwise, pass it up. The one dying with the most toys doesn't win, and we know it. So let's start acting like it.

There is a principle that follows these four.

5) Be whole-hearted in everything you do. Be in the present. This means that when you do something, do it with all your heart. Really do it. Don't just go through the motions, don't do it with one eye on the clock, or a fork in your hand, or half of your brain thinking about what happened an hour ago, or what will happen an hour from now. Really be in that activity. You can see how the first four principles support this one. If you are doing what you love doing, with people you love and admire and who bring you joy, in a simpler, slower, quieter life, surrounded with things that you love, then being whole-hearted in everything you do will be much easier. You will naturally be whole-hearted, because you will be very involved in what you are doing, interested in it, and getting joy and bliss from being involved in it. You will start living more and more in the present, less and less

in the past and future. Your focus will get sharper, your results better, and your body and soul calmer. This is a great antidote to the bustle of our lives these days.

Well, I have gone on enough here, haven't I? Even for a last letter. Thank you all for coming to Ireland. I knew you would, and it means a lot to me that we could share this time together, and that you would listen as I tried to capture the insights and principles that have been welling up in me these last few months. Dying, indeed, has opened up my receptors and I see and hear so much better now.

Do not doubt that I am with you on this Irish hilltop, and I am giving you all the love that spirit has to offer. A love that, I already know, is beyond our imagination or ability to describe.

I am truly blessed to have known the three of you. I love you all.

In Spirit and Love,

   Elton

P.S. Maire and I talked this over, but I wanted to announce it here. (You know my flair for dramatics.) Maire and I would like to offer the job of President of Full Spirit Brewery to...(trumpet call here please)...MJ...

We truly hope she will accept and come to Arizona.

Jack and Sarah, you didn't know this because MJ did not want any publicity about it, but after I sent my business plan out a few years ago detailing the "spirit and soul" aspects of Full Spirit for potential investors and employees, I got a note from MJ that simply said,

"I believe in you and all that you stand for Elton, and I want to put my money where my heart is."

Enclosed was a check for $103,000, which she had accumulated through Body Shop stock options and her store profits the previous five years. I knew that was probably all her savings and security, so I called to talk her out of it, or at least reduce it. But she just kept saying, "I believe in you, Elton. And I want my investments to reflect my beliefs."

Of course, we needed the money badly; almost exactly that amount would put us over the hump and make it all a go. It was like an angel had sent us what was necessary to follow our bliss. An angel named MJ.

So, MJ already is a large stakeholder in Full Spirit Brewing Company. Her retail experience will help our retail business at the Brewery, and her enthusiasm, imagination, and people skills will help us open up new marketing opportunities, joint ventures, and, in general, spread the Full Spirit SPIRIT far and wide. And her spirit has been nurtured as an employee in an organization that values spirit—The Body Shop—and she has practiced nurturing spirit in her own store. Her spirit and our spirit are in perfect tune. So what do you say MJ? Make my day and say you'll do it, then call Maire tonight with the good news. And, of course, Maire will remain as Chief Operating Office and Treasurer, and she is excited about the possibility of working with you on a daily basis.

P.P.S. Remember that night in The Gatehouse when we offered to help MJ figure out her career plan? Our first idea was that to help her do that we needed to know more about her. So we asked what MJ stood for. Of course, she wouldn't tell us, but after a while I convinced her that she needed a "partner" to share the secret with and take the pressure off her. I recommended me, and eventually she agreed. Jack and Sarah, you got three guesses to try and get it and failed.

Now, over the years, others have tried to wheedle the secret out of me, usually led by Jack, who pumped me for info after buying me a few ales. I did appreciate the ales but, as you all know, I never cracked.

But now we have a new dilemma. MJ needs a new partner to support her in keeping the secret. I have a suggestion. How about two new partners? After all, it'll probably take two of you to replace me. . . just kidding, just kidding. But, as close as we have been, it seems like it's time to have everyone in on this together. So, another question for you, MJ. Shall we form a new partnership? If you say yes, then have Jack go to the next page and continue reading. If no, then this is it and I'll say goodbye. Take your time, MJ, I'll wait.

I stopped reading and tilted my head towards MJ. Tears were rolling down her face.

"Don't mind these," she said wiping her hand across her cheek. "I'm really happy. I'd love to work with Maire at Full Spirit and it is really special remembering how Elton talked me into divulging my name, and then kept the secret all these years. He was so sneaky and so very sweet." She laughed lightly.

"And, you know, I think the sweet and sneaky parts are coming out today, too. Of all the days for me to let the secret out, I think Elton knows this might be the one. First, just being here in his homeland; second, hearing his wonderful message; third, offering me the President's job at the Brewery; and, finally, if I say no, the letter's over and Elton stops talking to us."

She shook her head and laughed again. "OK, Elton, you sneaky cuss, you win."

MJ turned to me. "Read on, Jack, and welcome to you and Sarah—my new partners."

I smiled my own smile of love and sadness. "I've waited a long time for this, MJ. All those years of trying to cajole it out of you and Elton, calling your partner at your store and pretending to be an insurance agent so she would tell me, snooping in your mail when I visited your house..."

"Jack!" Sarah interjected, "you went through her mail?"

I shrugged. "I was obsessed. But all to no avail. Finally, though, here it is."

I turned the page.

Good choice, MJ. You three will be a great trio. One small catch, Jack and Sarah. 22 years ago, I promised MJ I would never tell. And even with her permission now, I don't want to break that promise. So I'm going to go back to the original night when you made the three guesses and remind you of a few things I said. In fact, that night I gave you all the clues to get it yourselves, but you failed to take notice. So let's replay that night and think a bit more carefully. MJ will tell you when you figure it out.

Your first guess that night was "Missy Jo." And I said, "I cannot tell a lie. You are wrong."

Then you tried Mabel June and I said, "My pride and prejudice will only allow me to answer this guess one way."

Jack, you said, "What does pride and prejudice have to do with it? Just tell me if we're right."

And I replied, "It has everything to do with it."

And it does. With those guesses and my responses you have all the data you need to solve the mystery of MJ's name. So go to it. Start reading again when you get it right.

Sarah gazed at me with an inquisitive eyebrow. "So, Jack, all these years later, shall we huddle?"

"Huddle?" I said puzzled. Then suddenly I remembered. I had called for us to huddle the first time in order to plan our guesses…and so I could get a little closer to Sarah. I couldn't believe she remembered that. Was it a sign that this time it was her calling for the huddle, or was I just indulging in wishful thinking?

"Sure, let's huddle," I said. "Maybe all our years of experience will have made us better huddlers."

She smiled and scooted towards me and we "huddled."

I'm not sure if it was because I was reveling in the huddle so much that I wasn't thinking, or maybe she is just smarter than me, but it was Sarah who jumped back and let out an exclamation.

"Of course, it's so obvious. Why didn't I notice that 22 years ago? Jack, do you see it?"

"It's coming, Sarah," I said convincingly, "but you go ahead and start."

"It's all in Elton's responses. After our first guess, he said, 'I cannot tell a lie.' Who else said that?"

"Who said, 'I cannot tell a lie'?" I asked.

"Yes!"

"Well, George Washington, right?"

"Right, Jack. But neither George nor Washington helps with the initials 'MJ.' Go a step further. Like to the woman in George's life..."

"Aha," I shouted. "Martha Washington! The 'M' stands for Martha."

We turned to MJ for confirmation. She nodded slowly and smiled the smile of an old secret finally coming out.

"Yes!" I shouted.

"Now," Sarah continued, "after our second guess Elton said, 'my pride and prejudice will only allow me to answer this guess one way.' You correctly picked up that there was something funny about that response, Jack, and you questioned Elton asking what pride and prejudice has to do with it. But we ignored his response that it 'has everything to do with it.' That was our mistake. The answer was right in front of us all the time."

"I got it," I shouted. "Pride and Prejudice, Jane Austen's book. So the 'J' is Jane. MJ stands for Martha Jane!!"

"Bravo," MJ said. "It is Martha Jane. Now promise me that as good partners you'll never let that out."

"I promise," Sarah said, "but really, I don't know why. I think it's a beautiful name."

"Me too, MJ," I piped in. "I like it."

"Well, great," MJ said, "but keep it to yourself. Remember, you're my partners now. Now let's read the rest of Elton's letter."

I picked the letter up and searched for my place. As I did, I reflected on Elton's sneakiness and wisdom. In his last "P.S." of his last letter, Elton had taken the focus off him and put it on us. Us **together**. Us as partners for the future. As his life ended, he was ensuring that our lives would be intertwined and our support mechanisms for the future would be solidly in place. Just another reason to love the guy from Ireland. I found the passage and began.

> *Congratulations one and all. Pretty good hints, eh, Jack? Last time I gave them you may not have been totally focused on the task at hand, if you know what I mean.*

My cheeks colored. I knew what he meant. Sarah. Elton had never mentioned anything about my interest in Sarah before. Perhaps he had known more than he had let on. I read on quickly before the others could think about his meaning.

> *So, you're partners now and it is time for me to say goodbye again.*

> *I love you all and shall be with you always,*

> *Elton*

eighteen
chapter

I needed some time alone. Time to say goodbye again. I walked
to a railing along the edge of the cliff looking northeast at the
Irish Sea and Dublin. Some tourists had joined us on the hilltop and I moved away from their "oohs" and ahs" and clicking
cameras and found a private spot near the end of the rail. I took
a few deep breaths and wished to myself that I could see Elton
just one more time. The sea was brilliant and shining, an ethereal mist floated above the town, and the tops of the church
steeples glistened. I leaned forward, folded my arms on the rail
and took in the scene. Maybe this mixture of nature and God
was Elton's way of giving me a message.

I could hear MJ and Sarah speaking softly as they
approached. I twisted my neck and looked at their faces. Sad,
but somehow peaceful. Elton's message had gotten through.
There was hope for the future and we all felt Elton would,
somehow, be a part of it.

"Are you ready, Jack?" Sarah asked and she held out her hand
as she approached. Her eyes flashed and I saw the possibilities of
her question. Perhaps I was reading too much into it, but there
was only one way to find out. I nodded. I was ready. For a lot of
things. I turned the rest of my body reaching out a hand towards
her, my other hand securing a hard grip on the rail. As I pushed
off, a chunky young boy—maybe twelve—hit the rail with a
whoop and a jump, ignoring his parents' cries of caution. The rail
buckled, the anchor directly beneath me snapped and I began to
fall back. I thought the push I had made off the rail—tempered
though it was by the rail's collapse—might allow me to gain my
balance. But as I fought to get my weight towards the plateau and
away from the cliff, the boy bounced into me. He had hit the rail

on an angle and ricocheted, his momentum still enough that he was going off the cliff. Instinctively, I redirected my free arm, caught him and pushed him back. As he twirled in that state of tenuous balance, his dad arrived, snatching his shirt with a thrust and yanking him backwards to safety.

Meanwhile, Newton's first law of motion was working on me: for every action there is an equal and opposite reaction. Pushing the boy away from the cliff had thrown my momentum back towards the cliff's edge. As my upper body tilted and my weight shifted back, Sarah—her hand still outstretched—jumped towards me, her internal senses desperately trying to calculate how fast she could go without overshooting the mark and sliding off the cliff herself. My hand was still out from my push on the boy, and suddenly her hand was only inches away. She dug her heels as she hit the ground, trying desperately to brace her feet for the leverage she would need to pull me back. Rocks sprayed by me as her feet slid to a stop and as our fingertips touched— ever so lightly, I knew. From my years of athletics, from my boyhood Tai Chi with Grandfather, from my many losing bouts with Elton's hammock, I knew when balance was lost, when weight and gravity and angles and momentum were against you. I knew in that moment that grabbing Sarah's hand would not stop me; it would only begin her own inexorable slide over the edge. I pulled my hand away and pushed off backwards up and out over the chasm. Far enough from Sarah so she would have no thoughts of reaching or lunging for me—far enough away from her so she would be safe. And in some kind of universal reward, far enough away from the cliffside that the small oasis of trees would be my landing area, not the rocky abutments directly below.

Perhaps it was my altruistic act. Done without thinking. Without thinking of any benefits for me. Without any "filtering." Without looking for approval from anyone or anything. An act against my own instincts for self-preservation. An act of love unfettered by the weight of anything else. Perhaps that was what gave me the peaceful feeling. For I did feel peaceful. Even as I was falling. But it seemed like a dream, slow motion tumbling. A kaleidoscope of colors spun by, the green of the trees, the aqua blue of the ocean bouncing off the brown of the rocks, and the bright blue and white of the sky framing the cliff's edge with the faces peering down—Sarah and MJ among them. Their faces were getting smaller and smaller but slowly, so slowly. Maybe it was a dream.

"It's not a dream," a voice said urgently. "Focus on the trees. Go through the branches and grab, scratch, claw, pull at them. You must slow your descent."

I hit the trees reaching and suddenly the speed shifted, the limbs slashed and battered, softening me for the vicious punch of the brown dirt that took my breath. I wasn't spinning any more, which was sad; I liked spinning, the colors so beautiful, drizzled on the earth's canvas as I turned—now fading to black.

"Jack, Jack," I heard a voice say. "It is over. You have finished your story. Can you hear me?"

The voice surprised me. I was lost somehow, the story had become so real that I felt as if I had re-lived it, not just related it. I tried to clear my head and focus.

"Sandor, is that you?"

"Yes, Jack, welcome back. You were so deep into your story I thought you might not return."

"It seemed so real. The emotions so sharp and defined."

"Your story was strong. And insightful. You did indeed act out of love when you pulled away from Sarah. You listened to your heart. And in that concern and deep love for her, you may have saved yourself."

I thought about that for a minute. "Is that some kind of parable? By saving myself, do you mean literally, like I saved my life and I am alive and well, or figuratively, like I have saved my soul or something?"

"Maybe both. Not that your soul needed saving, but your growth as a person and as a spiritual being from such an act is great.

"And as for saving your life, that push off the cliff may have done it. Directly below the cliff are rocks. Landing on them would mean certain death. Your jump back to save Sarah sent you far enough away from the edge to land in the small, thick grove of trees."

Something was nagging at me. "Sandor, you keep saying 'may.' My concern for Sarah 'may' have saved my life; the push off the cliff 'may have done it.' What's up with all the 'mays?' Am I alive—in an earth sense—or not?"

"Yes, you are alive."

"Great," I exclaimed. Finally some answers to my questions. "So where am I?"

"You are exactly where your story left you."

I was confused. "You mean, at the bottom of the cliff?"

"Yes" he said.

I was still confused. "Why am I still there? Shouldn't I be in a hospital or something? Why haven't Sarah and MJ and the people on the cliff come down for me? Where are the paramedics?"

"They are all on their way."

"What has taken so long?"

"It has only been a few minutes."

"A few minutes? But I told you my whole life story. That had to take hours."

"Time is different here."

"Where's here? I thought you said I was alive."

"You have been alternating between being alive here on earth and not being alive here on earth. Earlier, when you asked, you were alive."

"And now…" I said haltingly, but I already knew. My eyes cleared suddenly and I saw myself lying below, under the trees. Sarah and MJ and others were just reaching my body.

"He's not breathing," someone shouted, and I saw Sarah quickly straddle my body and begin CPR. The father of the boy was emerging from the trail onto the beach, his face a mixture of relief and desperate concern. The mother was still halfway up the trail, carefully picking her way down, a tight grip on her son. Down the beach an emergency truck slid to a stop at the end of the access road and uniformed personnel jumped from the truck and began running towards me carrying trauma kits and a stretcher. But it didn't really feel like me anymore, that body under the trees. Things were getting farther away. I seemed to be moving up and out, faster and faster, my prone figure receding as Sarah continued her rhythmic cadence.

The speed increased as I turned away from the scene below and moved quickly towards a light in the distance. I shot forward and the light became richer and brighter, surrounding me in a long tunnel. Abruptly I slowed, my feet felt solid ground and I began to walk towards the source of the light. Suddenly I knew what was happening! I was having a near death experience.

I couldn't believe it. *I* was having a near death experience! I hadn't read any of those popular books on near death experiences, and frankly thought they were written by folks with a bit too much space left vacant in the upstairs loft. But it didn't feel funny or strange or unreal. It felt natural, somehow. And as for me, I felt fine, excellent actually. This near death thing wasn't so bad, and it sure beat the alternative—near death without the near.

I began to walk faster, anxious to know what the light held. The tunnel of light opened up and I saw three beings of light ahead of me. I say "beings of light" only because there was no other way to describe them. They were human in a sense; I saw hands and feet and human faces. But they shimmered and shined and I could almost see through them. They were radiant and luminous, and when they reached out their hands to me I went. I felt love and warmth and no fear.

They led me down a hall that had doors on all sides. It was clear that these doors were connected to me in some way, and the words over the doors surprised me. One said "World Leader," and I looked over to them in confusion.

"These are all paths you could have chosen," the middle being said. "The doors were open to you, but you did not choose to go through." As I continued to stare, they smiled and went on.

"You are capable of so much more than you allow yourself. You can make a huge difference in the world—much more than you have already made—but you must believe in yourself, follow your heart, and understand what is important. It is not riches, although that is there and available," and he pointed to an open door holding untold wealth.

"It is not fame or power or titles or how many people you have in your organization." I wanted to get defensive about that as he was striking too close to home, but that kind of emotion just didn't seem available.

"Your spiritual growth and corresponding love of fellow humans, and of all life, and of the earth, are what is important. When pure thoughts of love fill your consciousness, you will act with the best interests of all in mind. You must ensure that spirit is in you, your home, your workplace, your community, and the world. You must start where you can and with those you can affect. Radiate spirit out from you, and help open the door for others to see it, feel it and live it." The being paused and the focus on me intensified.

"What is your job on earth, Jack?"

I thought this might be a trick question. If anyone else had asked me that, the answer would have been immediate, "I am a CEO for a major manufacturing and services company." But this "being of light" wasn't just anyone. It was clearly an angel, or spiritual guide, or piece of God, or maybe all three. So, I wasn't sure whether "CEO," or person who is "ensuring that spirit is in me, my workplace, my community, and the world" was the right answer. And another thing I wasn't sure about was what to call this being. "Sir," and "Ma'am," sounded dumb, "Your Holiness" or

"Master" sounded strange to me also. The being seemed to be reading my mind as I furiously thought of all these things and held up a hand with a smile.

"There are no trick questions, Jack. I was thinking of your profession on Earth. And names aren't important at this time."

It hit me quickly, the voice, the inflections. "Sandor, that's you, isn't it?"

"It is not necessary for you to know at this time."

Now I was sure. "Sandor, that is you. Unless all spiritual beings use that same annoying phrase." I thought I heard a chuckle from the being on the left but before I could pursue it, Sandor—at least what I thought was Sandor—spoke again.

"Please answer the question, Jack. What is your job on earth? And this is not a trick question."

"OK, Sandor. We'll play it your way a little longer. The answer to your question is that I am a CEO for a major manufacturing and services firm."

Sandor nodded thoughtfully.

"And when you make a decision, how many people does it affect in the company?"

"Usually all of them, in one way or another," I replied.

"Earlier," Sandor continued, "I said you must start where you can and with those you can affect in bringing spirit to the world. You, Jack, can affect a large number of people. You are a CEO. You are the modern day equivalent of a tribal leader, or warrior chief. Many, many people's lives are affected on a daily basis by what you do. Feel this, Jack. Feel it deeply." He paused to let the weight of that enter me fully.

"Your passion is there for those people, Jack, but you have been afraid to let it out. Afraid you might look different, or foolish, afraid it might block your advancement, or lose you an award. But the goal is not advancement or awards; it is to touch people's lives in a wonderful, positive, spiritual way. And you have that opportunity in a big way, Jack. Not only for your company, but to be a model for other companies to follow, and other CEOs to follow. Are you with me, Jack?"

I nodded, a bit dazed, but with a growing comprehension. "I think so. I think I'm starting to see..." Sandor cut in here.

"Good Jack, let yourself see. Open up and soak in the truth. And think on this also. Work is now the major part of most people's lives. You spend more time there than in any other single place. If that experience is not uplifting to the spirit, or worse, if it is squashing the spirit, then the enlightenment of each individual, the growth of joy, the joining of all of us on earth together in spirit will not happen. You and other leaders in the workplace must be strong and fearless in your creation of a work environment that is joyous, an environment that upholds and uplifts the spirit.

"And, by the way, profits go way up when you do this. An energized workforce that is overflowing with spirit and aliveness will outperform others by great margins. This is the key competitive advantage for the new millennium."

My face must have lit up for Sandor stopped and waited for me to speak. "That's what Elton said. About the energized and passionate workforce being the key competitive advantage for the new millennium."

Sandor smiled. "I know. He was listening."

"To you?"

"Of course, and to many others in the spiritual realm. We do have an active interest, and play as big a part as your world will let us. You must listen though, or you won't hear." He paused again before continuing. "You are listening now, but this is an extreme way to communicate." I nodded agreement with that. "Listen each day. Take time out to be quiet and allow the communication to come through. Trust your instincts.

"Now follow your path, Jack, and use the special talents you have been given. The time is now." He paused and looked at me. "Come forward."

I moved towards him and suddenly everything was in focus. The middle being stepped forward. I could see him—or was it a her—clearly. It looked majestic and peaceful, calm and powerful. Not a face I recognized but the presence was familiar, the comfort strong.

"I am Sandor," it said. "Spiritual being, guide to many humans, worker for the earth—and frequent speaker of annoying phrases to humans."

This time the chuckle from the being on the left was more like a full-scale guffaw. I turned that way and fell to my knees in disbelief. It was Elton. Brilliant in his light, luminous and radiant and shimmering—but Elton nonetheless. His eyes twinkled as they met mine and his hand rose in greeting.

"I bet when I told you in Phoenix that I would see you again you didn't think it would be this soon, did you?"

I could only shake my head. Tears sprung from my eyes. "You're all right," I choked out.

"Of course. And I will be with you."

"As will I," the being on the right said. I turned that way.

"Grandfather?"

"Yes, my child."

I lost it, then. It was all too much. I sobbed uncontrollably, looking from one to the other in disbelief, gratitude and love. They comforted me. Without moving, they seemed to extend themselves and I was enveloped within their light. The feeling was astonishing, as if pure love and warmth was being transferred to my body and soul. As I regained control I looked at Grandfather and suddenly felt the shame and guilt of my betrayal many years ago.

"Grandfather, I am sorry for turning my back on you and your customs when I was a boy. My lack of respect was…"

He waved me to a stop. "I accept your apology, my son. Do not think about it any further. Guilt is the most useless of emotions. You were a boy. You have grown into a fine man. As Sandor said, you can make such a difference in the world. Channel your energies there."

"So, I am going back. This is a 'near death' experience, not just a death experience?"

Sandor nodded.

"Now go," he said. "It is time to begin your work." I began to float back the way I had come, then Sandor moved quickly forward and held up a hand. I stopped and Sandor leaned a little closer.

"Oh, and try eating a little bit better. You know, fruits, fiber, vegetables—and barley and hops in your beer, or an olive in your martini doesn't count. Maybe try a little exercise, keep off the cigars, and drink more water. That should make you feel better." As I turned to go Sandor added in a stage whisper:

"Breath won't be so bad either…"

I jerked around but before I could say anything I noticed they were all laughing, Elton most of all. He was practically falling over. I started to laugh too, thinking all we needed was a couple of snorts from MJ and we'd all lose it totally.

"Okay," I said putting my hands on my hips in a mock angry pose. "Very funny, Sandor." None of them showed any signs of stopping. Maybe they didn't need MJ. "You know," I continued," I didn't think wise guys were a part of whatever you call this place."

"Call it whatever you like," Sandor said. "Heaven, nirvana, the other side of the veil. And humor is a big part. It isn't fire and brimstone or even Lawrence Welk music with bubbles. It's wonderful, loving, fun, and funny. Just like it can be down there. If you let it."

His eyes intensified. "Now go back and bring the love and spirit to all you can."

I started moving again, and I gazed at them all as I traveled. Elton raised his hand then turned his thumb up in the same move as when I had wheeled him out of the hospital. Grandfather bowed lightly while Sandor opened his arms, seemingly shooting love out at me. I began to go faster and faster, and the light faded until it became dark, although I was still warm. Then I felt heaviness, and weight, then suddenly pain. My whole body seemed to hurt, and I was aware of my breathing for the first time since the fall. Each breath was like fire, pain spreading through my chest and down my legs. I opened my eyes and slowly they focused. MJ and Sarah were peering down at me as the emergency personnel arrived.

"Jack," they said in unison and I could feel them gripping each of my hands. I am not sure how I looked, but their expressions changed and they looked harder into my eyes.

"Jack?" they said again, but this time it was more of a question as they tried to read a face that had been touched by spirit. I opened my mouth and out came the words.

"I've been somewhere very special and we have much to do."

epilogue

My cheery Irish doctor tells me I'll be well enough to leave the hospital tomorrow and fly back home. It has been an interesting four weeks. I can't say I've enjoyed my stay exactly, not with tubes and needles poking into me and lousy hospital food—albeit Irish—served three times a day. But it did give me a lot of uninterrupted time to think—more uninterrupted time than I've ever had in my life. That kind of quiet time, if you can stay quiet and focused, is truly a gift. I am seeing things more clearly now—the path I must follow, and the courage I must demonstrate.

I have looked for further guidance from Sandor, closing my eyes hard to try to see him, hear him, and feel him. So far, nothing. There are mixed opinions on my experience and on who or what Sandor is. MJ thought it very cool; Sarah believed it was very real. The doctor thought it was a hallucination, but "nothing to worry about." I told Maire how I had seen Elton and how good he looked. She cried and held my hand and said "thank you."

I don't think I'll tell too many other people about my near death experience—certainly not the Board of Directors or the top executives of Dynamics. But what will they think when I return and begin to focus my attention on transforming the workplace and inspiriting our workforce? Will they believe me when I say that a motivated, passionate workplace will be the key business discriminator of the 21st century? Will they fight me if I push to forego short-term profits in order to nurture our workforce and build the trust that has started to slip away?

How far will I be able to go and still keep control of the company? How will I convince enough key players that *my* way—inspired by my friends, family, visions, and intuition—is the *right* way? That doing the right thing and doing the profitable thing are not mutually exclusive? And what specifically will I do? *How* will I rebuild the trust and inspirit our workforce?

Many questions. So far my forced rest hasn't provided the answers. But it has heightened my resolve and solidified my commitment. I am ready to go. Ready to take all the things I have learned and build the plan. I'll let you know how this next chapter plays out. I hope I don't have to write that from a hospital bed.

But what about from a honeymoon suite?

That's my other promise to myself. To have courage in my personal life. To face my fears and insecurities and open up time for the truly important people in my life—Elizabeth and Sarah. To be there for Elizabeth more as father and friend. And to be open, honest and truly myself with Sarah. Show her that the "new" me would be a wonderful partner.

Whew! Those are big tasks. Changing the "work me" and my company; and changing the "personal me" to be the best father I can be and to win Sarah as my own.

Wish me luck as I start down *my* path.

And I wish you the courage and heart to go down *yours*. As you lead with your heart you will find others seeking to live as you do. Together, all of us will make a difference.

And now, it's time to begin...

About the author

Craig Elkins has worked for U.S. Intelligence, been a professional bowler, wrote comedy scripts, been a Director of Quality Assurance at The Boeing Company, and founded The Applied Thinking and Creativity Team at that same company. Still searching for the unique contribution he could make to the world, he visited Ireland on his fortieth birthday and had an epiphany. The next day he began The Gatehouse: A Book about Business, A Story about Life. Once he was "on his path" the doors and windows flew open. Writers such as Martin Rutte and Maida Rogerson of Chicken Soup for the Soul at Work fame; Patricia Aburdene—Megatrends 2000; and Diane Dreher—The Tao of Inner Peace, The Tao of Womanhood, and The Tao of Personal Leadership, all offered their help in getting The Gatehouse: A Book about Business, A Story about Life off the ground. Writing and publishing the book was a wonderful, if arduous process, filled with the joy of creating as well as the many rejections from agents, editors and publishers who felt the book too "different."

Craig and his team at The Gatehouse Alliance have recently developed two workshops based on the book. These workshops are very different from the normal corporate training experience, using the book's characters and settings to create a very special and memorable day. One workshop supports those in leadership roles trying to create an inspirited, passionate workforce and the other is for everyone and focuses on your individual experience of work and life. Craig also speaks and consults on Spirit in the Workplace, Leadership, Teamwork and Communication, Creativity, and Intellectual Capital and is currently at work on the second book in The Gatehouse series.

For more ∎ **information**

For more information on The Gatehouse Workshops or other concepts and tools in the book such as The Six Thinking Hats, please see the website at **www.thegatehousebook.com** and/or send me an e-mail at **info@thegatehousebook.com**.

If you have any thoughts, comments, or suggestions—or stories from your own experiences that you would like to share—please send me an e-mail. I'd love to hear from you.